Mindfulness and Wellbeing for Student Learning

Mindfulness and Wellbeing for Student Learning

A guided 5-week course

*Lorraine Millard, Louise Frith
and Patmarie Coleman*

Open University Press

Open University Press
McGraw Hill
Unit 4,
Foundation Park
Roxborough Way
Maidenhead
SL6 3UD

email: emea_uk_ireland@mheducation.com
world wide web: www.openup.co.uk

First edition published 2023

A catalogue record of this book is available from the British Library

ISBN-13: 9780335251063
ISBN-10: 0335251064
eISBN: 9780335251070

Library of Congress Cataloging-in-Publication Data
CIP data applied for

Typeset by Transforma Pvt. Ltd., Chennai, India

Praise Page

"*I am so glad that this book has been written! I helped to run many five week Mindfulness courses for anxious Bioscience undergraduate students, with Lorraine as the mindfulness lead, from 2016 to 2019. Based on answers to questionnaires and emails, I can vouch for the fact that this carefully planned course yielded tangible benefits in calming students when facing exams or oral presentations, and they also taught their friends the mindfulness tools that they had learnt with Lorraine. This book is invaluable for others wanting to set up mindfulness provision in their academic institutions. The boxes with suggested activities are excellent as are the scripts for body scans etc. A highly practical book, easily accessible for others to use with their students.*"

Dr Elisabeth Curling, Senior Lecturer in Immunology,
School of Biosciences, University of Kent, UK

"*This book is beautiful and clear. It introduces mindfulness in an easy and practical way, explaining how it can address some of the typical patterns which can interfere with student well-being. It brings the best of several longer evidence-based mindfulness courses into a bite-sized 5 week course for students. It is very accessible and well-structured. It will enable students across the globe to improve their well-being. Highly recommended.*"

Dr Julia Ronder, Consultant Child and
Adolescent Psychiatrist

"*Due to the big success, we will be running our Mindfulness course again. Having the book to recommend to students will be of great help!*"

Adelina Gschwandtner, Senior Lecturer in Economics,
University of Kent, UK

"*This book is a fascinating and practical guide to mindfulness for students. I would thoroughly recommend reading it if you are a student yourself, or an educator looking to help students with their mental wellbeing. Packed with a wealth of knowledge and experience, this book also provides a useful workbook for anyone developing a mindfulness programme for students.*"

Dr Jacqueline Buchanan, GP Partner and
medical student educator

"*This book offers an accessible introduction to mindfulness for young people with the specific challenges of student life, especially in the current world. The book is a valuable guide to mindfulness, tailored for students, drawing key ideas and practices from mindfulness experts. The authors' depth of experience working with university students is evident in this book, meeting both students themselves and mindfulness teachers. The students' stories really bring alive the relevance of mindfulness for college students."*

Sarah Silverton, Mindfulness Teacher and Trainer,
The Present Courses CIC

"This is a unique book that is a joy to read. Importantly, it is grounded by a wonderful collaboration between a community that includes university students, teaching staff and practitioners. It brings together key elements of mindfulness practice into a short course that can be followed by anyone. The content is informed by personal experience and by published research. There are exercises to build good habits and tips for managing expectations. Most importantly, the content is knitted together through an attitude of reflective practice and compassionate acceptance. I would recommend this book to anyone wanting to learn about mindfulness. The advice provided encourages a way of living that can transform one's inner life and help to build communities that understand and value the ever-changing world we live in."

Dr Dinkar Sharma, Reader in Psychology,
School of Psychology, University of Kent, UK

Contents

Acknowledgements

Like all projects, the Mindfulness Project at Kent would not have flourished without the support of the institution, specifically the Learning and Development Team and the Wellbeing Team. Mindfulness at Kent started when Lorraine ran an 8 week group for staff. The course flourished for several years, and the staff from these courses continued to keep mindfulness alive by creating monthly meet-ups and introducing mindfulness courses into their academic schools. Many colleagues have been involved along the way, but it is important to mention some key people: Dr Lis Curling, Nicola Urquart, Helen Caroline, Jackie Double and Dinkar Sahrma. The student involvement really took off because students know how to involve other students. Therefore, it is with huge gratitude that we mention the members of the first Kent mindfulness committee; Eszter Zsisku, Halapana Shritharan, Ijaz Aflah and Natalie Potts. And the members of this year's committee are; Asia Charles, Faith Turton, Joshua Stevens and Natalia Christini.

Introduction

What is mindfulness?

Mindfulness means paying attention in a particular way, on purpose, in the present moment, non-judgementally (Kabat-Zinn, 1994: 4). An important aspect that is central to the effectiveness of mindfulness is cultivating kindness to the self with patience and acceptance. This is especially important for students who are in a competitive environment and who might be particularly critical of themselves. The practice of mindfulness teaches us self-compassion and can help us to be less defensive, take responsibility and recover more quickly from life's upheavals and disappointments. This generates further compassion towards others and the world (Goleman et al., 2017). The word 'mindfulness' is most associated with Buddhism and is a system of practices to help people move towards enlightenment. Jon Kabat-Zinn created the 8-week Mindfulness Based Stress Reduction (MBSR) course, a secular course designed to work with the particular stresses of modern life and people living with physical, emotional and mental pain. Mindfulness combines many of the skills taken from spiritual traditions together with modern psychology and neuroscience. This enables us to live our life with a greater sense of control and helps us cultivate greater happiness and satisfaction from life.

Mindfulness is a methodology to understand the mind and the body and our habitual reactions to life. Over the past 30 years, Mark Williams has developed Mindfulness Based Cognitive Therapy (MBCT) to help patients working with depression and anxiety. Mindfulness has been adapted to be used in many different areas, including in schools and universities. There has been much research validating its effectiveness to address some of the major issues of our time and issues that affect students, such as rumination, lack of focus, deregulated emotions and a repetitive wandering and worrying mind. Richard Chambers and his colleagues (2008) reported that mindfulness aids focus, concentration and working memory, which Williams and Penman (2010) believe it helps students to regulate the feeling of being overwhelmed.

This book is a 5-week introduction to mindfulness that has been adapted from longer programmes of mindfulness that include: Mindfulness Based Stress Reduction (Kabat-Zinn, 2013), Mindfulness Based Cognitive Therapy (Williams et al., 2011), Mindfulness in Schools (available online), The Present (Silverton, n.d., online) and Williams and Penman's (2010) 8 week programme, Mindfulness: A Practical Guide to Finding Peace in a Frantic World. It is aimed specifically at university and college students and has been developed over our years of practise with many different groups of students. We have found that the 5 week course is long enough for students to get a taste and insight into mindfulness practice, but it is not so long that students become disengaged. Mindfulness has been shown to support students' learning and to teach students how to manage stress and overcome anxieties, as well as help them to live more fully and happily in the present moment (De Bruin et al., 2014).

If you are reading this book with the intention of setting up a student mindfulness group, please bear in mind that there are times and circumstances in which mindfulness might not be appropriate, such as when a person is going through an acute mental health episode, or a difficult life event such as bereavement. This is why it is important to speak individually to each member of the group before starting the course to ensure that this is the right time for them, and where necessary that they have the correct support. However, mindfulness is useful for all aspects of life, and there are some specific 'pressure points' for students when mindfulness can be particularly useful. These are:

- **Focusing:** to help them study effectively
- **Developing confidence:** such as making new friends and building positive relationships
- **Dealing with stress:** such as giving a presentation or sitting an examination
- **Making decisions:** such as deciding which modules to choose or the next steps to take in life
- **Managing their time:** overcoming procrastination and making time for nourishing activities.

Furthermore, mindfulness can build a sense of belonging and provide students with a supportive community of practice. It is an effective way of dealing with the emotions and reactions that we all have as humans. Therefore, it is really important that group leaders are aware of and work at creating an atmosphere of inclusivity, acceptance and awareness of the politics of diversity.

This book has two aims. The first is to introduce a 5 week programme of mindfulness that teaches students to learn new ways to handle moods and emotions. This increases focus, concentration, productivity and compassion for self and others, in what can often be a demanding and competitive environment. It explains the principles behind self-care, so that students are able to live fuller, happier and healthier lives. Students will be encouraged to develop the ability to approach all experiences, whether they are good, bad or neutral, pleasant or unpleasant, without being judged. The focus of the mindfulness practice is to become aware of the small changes in the physical sensations of the body, in what is happening in the world around us and in thoughts, emotions and moods. This 5 week programme encourages development of the skill of awareness of experiences from moment to moment. This is done with an attitude of acceptance, rather than avoidance, so that students learn to respond with more awareness to situations rather than simply reacting automatically. Each of the 5 weeks of learning about mindfulness includes reading, meditation, movement, reflection, exercises and daily life practices. It is useful to keep a daily record of the experience of practices and exercises, to facilitate reflection throughout the course. Like all things, the more you practise, the more you gain, as when developing a muscle or new habit. Therefore, commitment to practise, even for just a few minutes a day, can create significant change. The programme encourages students to focus on the present and not to get caught up in a constant stream of thoughts, helping them to be really present in the moment. The book also focuses on the ways in which mindful practice can support students' development of academic skills. Overall, the programme is helpful in dealing with ongoing difficulties and the attitudes that we bring to these.

The second aim of this book is to provide a teaching resource to anyone wishing to set up a mindfulness group in a university or college setting. Although mindfulness can be practised alone, it is often much more effective when undertaken as part of a group. This is because the group offers regular practice and support to its members, which has a positive impact on the daily practice that students undertake on their own. This is similar to learning a musical instrument, which requires regular lessons and daily practice, as do yoga and learning a foreign language. Therefore, each chapter contains teaching notes and lesson plans so that you can set up a mindfulness group wherever you are. It is important to note that in order to teach mindfulness, you must have completed a mindfulness course yourself and have a regular mindfulness practice. Completing a mindfulness teacher training course will further support you with facilitating the group. It is essential that you have supervision, preferably with a BAMBA-registered mindfulness teacher or a qualified and experienced mindfulness teacher (see the mindfulness good practice guidelines: BAMBA). It is also important that you have support from a clinical or mental health practitioner, if any difficulties of that nature arise in the group.

In the process of writing this book, two major events occurred that have had a significant impact on many students' emotional wellbeing. First, the COVID-19 pandemic hit the world; universities in the UK locked down and moved very quickly to online learning. This presented a significant challenge for us to shift weekly mindfulness sessions from rooms on campus to an online environment. We thought that the physical space and its atmosphere, eye contact and body language were integral to the success of campus mindfulness groups, so we were very unsure of how students would respond to the online mindfulness sessions. We didn't know whether students would attend and what impact mindfulness would have in a virtual environment. However, once we moved online, we realised that in some ways mindfulness sessions can work well online. The benefits are that students are in their own familiar environment, and they can attend easily because they don't have to go anywhere. In addition to the practical considerations, participation online can be effective because students can join in the group discussion with their cameras on, then turn them off during the meditation so they can really relax into individual mindfulness practice. This said, now that we have returned to face-to-face physical spaces with students, we really appreciate the sense of community and supportiveness of being in a group. Although online can work well, practising mindfulness together inperson provides some additional benefits, such as in-person connection, the journey to and from the group and the opportunity for informal contact amongst the group members.

The other significant development to occur during the process of writing this book is the recognition and acknowledgement of the persistent and pernicious impact of racism in society. This has surfaced since the deaths of George Floyd and Briana Taylor. For some, this awareness is a new and uncomfortable experience; for others, it is confirmation of an ongoing experience of being 'other'.

One outcome of these two major events has been the rise in the reporting of anxiety and depression among young people. In our own mindfulness groups and in this book, we take time to acknowledge the intersectionality of difference that many students experience acutely when they emerge from their home environment into a university setting. Intersectionality refers to an awareness of how a person's social and political identities – their gender, sex, race, colour, class, sexuality, religion, disability and neurodiversity – may combine and accentuate the experience of the different types of discrimination or privilege.

In 2021, The Prince's Trust Youth Index reported that 56 per cent of 16–24-year-olds reported 'always' or 'often' feeling anxious (Prince's Trust, 2021). These feelings can intensify during mindfulness practice, so it is useful for group leaders to be aware how national and international events can impact on wellbeing. Since 2020, attendance at online mindfulness sessions at our institution has increased and the students attending are more diverse; specifically, there have been more black students and students of colour, male students and international students attending than is usually the case at face-to-face mindfulness sessions. Providing a space where all students feel welcome and seen requires mindfulness group leaders to have an awareness of the politics of privilege and inequality, which the pandemic and Black Lives Matter have made more transparent. As we write this book, the pandemic continues and some restrictions are still in place. Although we are all enjoying being together on campus again, it seems likely that universities will retain a blended approach to some elements of teaching and supporting students. Therefore, the book also aims to provide guidance on supporting both face-to-face and online mindfulness groups.

Motivation for mindfulness practice

Before starting to practise mindfulness, you may find it interesting and useful to write down your responses to the following questions. When you have completed the 5-week programme, you can then reflect on your original reasons for undertaking it.

1 What has drawn you to this 5 week mindfulness programme?
2 What are your expectations of mindfulness practice?
3 What do you want to be different by the end of this programme?
4 What do you want to get out of doing mindfulness?

Home practice

The patterns of the mind that you will be working to change have been around for a long time. These patterns are also frequently habitual and automatic. You can only succeed in making changes in these long-established ways of thinking if you put time and effort into learning new ways of doing so. It is challenging to make time to do the home practice that is part of this course. However, it really is worth it. It is useful to try to adopt an open mind to follow the course and practise as often as you can to see if mindfulness works for you. In order for you to decide whether this approach could be a useful part of your life, you need to engage with it fully over the 5 weeks. During this practice, you will reflect on your experiences of the home practice throughout the week. You will think about any difficulties that you may be experiencing with the practice itself. Much of the learning in mindfulness is drawn from your experiences, which you can learn to welcome with curiosity.

Facing difficulties

A central aim of the approach is to learn how to be more fully aware and present in each moment of life. The good news is that this makes life more enjoyable, interesting, vivid and fulfilling. On the other hand, it also means facing what is present, even when it is unpleasant and difficult. Depending on the events in your life and how you have been supported up until now, mindfulness may lead to feelings and emotions that are very hard for you to manage alone. In these circumstances, you should seek further support from a trained counsellor or university wellbeing practitioner/mental health adviser. Through mindfulness practice you will learn gentle ways to face difficulties. In the long run, you will find that acknowledging and learning to face difficulties is the most effective way to reduce unhappiness. Should you experience difficulties that aren't manageable, on your own, please do seek professional help.

Patience and persistence

As you will be working to change established patterns of thinking, much of the approach will involve investing considerable time and effort, the effects of which may only become apparent later. In many ways, this is much like studying: students need to read core texts, engage in discussions or lab/studio work, complete assignments and respond to feedback, sit exams or final assessments – and then wait patiently for the results. We encourage you therefore to approach this course with the same spirit of patience and persistence – by committing to put the time and effort into what will be asked of you, while accepting that the impact of your efforts might not be apparent straightaway.

Focusing on the breath and trauma-informed practice

A key focus for mindfulness is a focus on the breath, which is a constant anchor in the body. Williams and Penman (2010) give five reasons to use the breath as an anchor in mindfulness practice: first, its presence can be taken for granted; second, breathing happens automatically without us having to think about it, but we can tune into it; third, it is a natural rhythm to focus on during meditation; fourth, different breathing patterns indicate how you are feeling generally; and finally, the breath provides an anchor for your attention. Key to mindfulness is learning how to tune into your breath and focus on its energy. There are many ways to do this. Some people find it useful to place their hand on their belly to feel the breath moving the abdomen up and down, while others find it helpful to slow the breath down and feel it flowing in and out of the nostrils. You can try one of these techniques to engage with the breath.

The concept of 'coming to the breath' is something that we will keep returning to throughout this book. Whenever you need to ground yourself, it is useful to first settle your body, or as it is referred to in the Mindfulness in Schools Project (MISP), FOFBOC: Feet On Floor, Bottom On Chair. Push your back into the chair so that you are self-supporting with your head over your heart, your heart over your pelvis. It sometimes helps by trying to imagine a string coming out of the top of your head. Keep your eyes closed or have a soft downwards gaze and focus on your breath.

Over the past few years, mindfulness has developed to become increasingly more trauma informed. Trauma-informed practice provides other ways of focusing rather than using the breath, which can be difficult for some. It encourages you to prioritise listening to yourself above the guidance being given by the facilitator. The facilitator encourages you to make choices during the practice, and be guided by what feels right for you. Practice alternatives can include placing one hand on your heart and one hand on your belly. Alternatively, you can focus on your feet being in contact with the floor, your bottom on the chair, your body in contact with a surface. Also, the process of slowly opening and closing your hands provides another way of becoming more present with yourself. If closing your eyes is not for you, keeping a soft gaze or downwards glance can be an option.

Neuroscience connections

A recent discovery is that our brain is malleable. It used to be thought that after a certain age your brain was established for life, and people had firm personality traits such as optimist or pessimist, worrier or risk-taker. However, neuroscience has established that this is not the case; people may have some strong traits, but for the most part, a healthy brain has the flexibility to re-programme itself given the right amount of appropriate practice. This discovery introduced a new word into our vocabulary – *neuroplasticity* (Konorski, cited by Livingston,

1966). The brain's neuroplasticity and regular mindfulness practice enable us to have greater control over the stress response and our sense of threat. This enables us to be less reactive and more responsive.

Researchers have identified positive structural changes in various parts of the brain according to new skills we learn, such as learning a new language, a musical instrument or how to juggle. A good example of this are the changes recorded in the posterior hippocampus, which is the region of the brain associated with memory. For example, black-cab taxi drivers in London are required to pass the 'knowledge', a challenging and complex exam which requires them to memorise all of the streets in London in order to obtain a licence to drive a taxi. The posterior hippocampus is the part of the brain used for navigation and is considerably larger in London taxi drivers than members of the general population. They change significant parts of their brains through practice. This is also the case for people who are multilingual or who can play several musical instruments.

Although it is possible for the brain to change from anxious to calm, it takes practice to rewire the neuropathways. This is because we have developed the skill of 'automatic pilot', the skill that makes it possible for us to walk or drive and do numerous things at once without having to think about them. Unfortunately, we tend to apply the same automatic pilot mechanisms to our emotions, thoughts and body responses. This is why we find ourselves reacting to things from our past or because of habit, which obliterates the experiences of now. We do this in many ways. We decide what we like or don't like quite early on. We decide facts about ourselves which we think are truths, such as: 'I'm not popular', 'I'm not clever enough', 'I can't paint'. These ideas become entrenched in us, including waking up with that feeling of butterflies in the tummy that makes us anxious; it can signal anxiety, but it might also signal positive adrenaline. The truth might be that we are simply hungry or even excited about something.

Mindfulness enables us to challenge our old ideas, thoughts and reactions that no longer serve us and really pay attention to the now, so that we can interrupt the automatic pilot and move into the reality of the current situation. We are constantly making assumptions about the world based on past beliefs rather than the reality of now. This means that while we are preoccupied with our interpretation of events or processes such as getting to classes on time, we miss turning up for 'now' and the awareness of the natural beauty around us, or the opportunity of a warm connection with someone we sit next to on the bus or in class.

What we learn from this is, where we direct our attention is where our thoughts, our moods or body will go. Therefore, if we are preoccupied with the thought of being unpopular or a failure, we will spin around in a mist of ruminative thoughts about this, changing our mood into one of defensiveness or depression whilst twisting up our body through tension. However, if we place our attention at least for some of the time on the world around us, the opportunity for connection and the sounds and images we encounter, we might be moved to feel a lightness in mood and even notice the opportunity for a heart-warming interaction.

Figure 1: Attitudes to cultivate mindfulness (diagram by Joshua Stevens, Human Geography student)

Attitudes to cultivate mindfulness

There are some attitudes which help us to cultivate mindfulness. Take a look at the image reproduced as Figure 1 and reflect on your current feelings about these attitudes in yourself.

- What do you already feel quite familiar with?
- What attitudes are more difficult for you to relate to?

Structure of the book

This book is based on many years of experience working with students in mindfulness groups. We run courses throughout the year and often link them to key points in the student experience, such as; at the start of a new academic year to support students to overcome social anxiety; before a final assessment period to help students to manage exam-related stress; and during the writing-up phase of a dissertation or thesis to enable research students to make connections with others and stay motivated. The courses we run are generally 5 weeks long. This is because 5 weeks fits easily into an academic semester and gives students a solid introduction to mindfulness, but it is shorter than the more common 8 week mindfulness course. It is for this reason that this book is arranged in five chapters.

Each chapter contains a brief illustrative story about a student. These stories are based on students or a composite of students who we have worked with over the years. We have changed their names and sometimes adapted the stories to make our point clear and protect the students' identities. There is then an explanation of an aspect of mindfulness, followed by a description of practice and a meditation script. This is followed by reflection, then a lesson plan with teaching notes and homework. The lesson plans include aims, objectives and activities with timings for each section. The total time for each session is 90 minutes, but the timings within the sessions for each activity are approximate because they are dependent on the group and their input. Each chapter ends with some further resources and references. Over the years of working with students, we have gathered feedback and testimonials about the impact mindfulness has had on them. We have chosen just a few of these to publish in different chapters throughout this book.

The focus of Chapter 1 is bringing awareness of the moment. This supports students to develop the skills of being able to focus and maintain concentration, which is a fundamental aspect of successful study. Chapter 2 looks at the human habit of living in your head, or as Steven Covey puts it, realising that 'We see the world, not as it is, but as we are - or, as we are conditioned to see it' (Covey, 1989/2020: 28). This chapter teaches us about the importance of developing loving kindness to the self. The focus of Chapter 3 is staying present even when events in life become difficult or stressful and you feel that you may become overwhelmed with the pressure of academic work. Chapter 4 revisits the theme that thoughts are not facts, teaching us that mindfulness practice can help us to build in a pause in our thoughts, enabling us to make wise choices and support decision-making. The focus of Chapter 5 is on integrating mindfulness into our everyday lives. This helps us to remember to be in the moment, using the lessons learnt throughout the 5 week course and the anchor of the breath, the body or the self to maintain mindfulness practice beyond the course. The book closes with some reflections and thoughts taken from students we have worked with.

Student perspective 1

"As a psychology student, I have always been curious about the mind, its intricate functions and the mystery that surrounds it. It is not like any other body part; I believe it holds the soul and essence of humanity within it. Although I held this sense of wonder towards the mind before, mindfulness is the skill which truly unlocked a deeper desire to explore and understand my own mind, and appreciate that it is the only one which I have privileged, unique access to. For many years, I lived on autopilot, allowing the narrative of my life to be determined by my anxieties and my skittish thoughts, prone to spiralling out of control when left unchecked and unquestioned. It was through mindfulness that I was able to begin the journey of self-love and acceptance, that is now so fundamental to my belief system.

One thing I particularly love about mindfulness is that you're never done learning, making new discoveries and experiencing that profoundly satisfying 'click' when a teaching suddenly reveals a deeper meaning to you. This was definitely my experience of the 5 week mindfulness, which gave a new narrative to the meditations and teachings I was somewhat familiar with, and showed me how each mindful skill was built on another one, and could be linked to other teachings and practices. I found it especially profound to develop the ability to not only love myself, but to bring a kind and non-judgemental attitude to others in the world, even those who I may not be on the best terms with. This really brought home the message of mindfulness being a 'movement' for me, and I only hope it will continue to grow, as I truly think a more mindful world will be a happier, kinder place to live in." (Eszter Zsisku, Psychology student)

References

BAMBA (British Association of Mindfulness-based Approaches) Good Practice Guidelines for Teaching Mindfulness Courses https://bamba.org.uk/wp-content/uploads/2020/01/GPG-for-Teaching-Mindfulness-Based-Courses-BAMBA.pdf [accessed 12 October 2022].

Chambers, R., Chuen Yee Le, B. and Allen, N.B. (2008) The impact of intensive mindfulness training on attentional control, cognitive style, and affect, *Cognitive Therapy and Research*, 32 (3): 303–322.

Covey, S.R. (1989/2020) *The 7 Habits of Highly Effective People*. New York: Simon & Schuster.

De Bruin, E.I., Meppelink, R. and Bögels, S.M. (2014) Mindfulness in higher education: Awareness and attention in university students increase during and after participation in a mindfulness curriculum course, *Mindfulness*, 6 (5): 1137–1142.

Goleman, D., Boyatzis, R., Davidson, R.J., Druskat, V. and Kohlrieser, G. (2017) *Emotional Self-awareness: A Primer* (Building Blocks of Emotional Intelligence, Book 1). Florence, MA: More Than Sound.

Kabat-Zinn, J. (1994) *Mindfulness Meditation*. London: Piatkus Books.

Kabat-Zinn, J. (2013) *Full Catastrophe Living: Using the Wisdom of Your Body and Mind to Face Stress, Pain, and Illness*. New York: Bantam Dell.

Livingston, R.B. (1966) Brain mechanisms in conditioning and learning, *Neurosciences Research Program Bulletin*, 4 (3): 349–354.

Mindfulness in Schools Project. https://mindfulnessinschools.org/ [accessed 19 January 2021].

Prince's Trust (2021) https://www.princes-trust.org.uk/about-the-trust/news-views/tesco-youth-index-2021 [accessed 19 January 2021].

Silverton, S. (n.d.) *The Present Courses*. https://www.sarahsilvertonmindfulness.co.uk/the-present-courses/ [accessed 19 January 2021].

Williams, M. and Penman, D. (2010) *Mindfulness: A Practical Guide to Finding Peace in a Frantic World*. London: Piatkus Books.

Williams, M.J., McManus, F., Muse, K. and Williams, J.M.G. (2011) Mindfulness-based cognitive therapy for severe health anxiety (hypochondriasis): An interpretative phenomenological analysis of patients' experiences, *British Journal of Clinical Psychology*, 50 (4): 379–397.

1 Bringing awareness

Soni's story

Soni stumbled into her 10am lecture. She hadn't read the slides and hadn't thought about the subject since the last seminar, which she didn't understand or engage with.

She was feeling really tense as she walked towards the university building. Head bowed, she didn't want to speak to anyone. Feeling anxious and self-conscious she walked as fast as she could, just wishing to be at the top of the hill. She recognised a couple of people from her course, but she pretended she was on the phone so that she would not have to engage with them. In her head a story was unfolding in which nobody really liked her and they could all see that she had woken up late and, unlike them, had not prepared for class. She imagined them talking about her behind her back. When someone from her class came up behind her and smiled and said 'Hello', she quickly buried herself in her phone and just waved limply. By the time she was up the hill she had reminded herself of all the past friendships she had had that did not turn out well, and she was feeling both very sad and angry at why she always did this to herself and why no one really liked her.

Soni was feeling tired and hungry. Having overslept, she had left her flat in a hurry. Having told herself how bad and unlikeable she was, she hadn't wanted to talk to anyone in the shared kitchen. Now she was feeling pretty sick. She had had a bad night's sleep following a difficult conversation with her mum about not being able to get on with her studies, and they had ended up arguing. Now she felt bad about not trying hard enough and pushing her mum away.

She was feeling both guilty because she couldn't focus and stupid because she was struggling to understand the last seminar. She had put off reading the paper for this morning's seminar and to block out negative feelings she had binge-watched an American sitcom on Netflix until really late. Though too tired to read the paper, her head was spinning and she couldn't get to sleep for some time. Unfortunately, this was becoming the norm. Having got to the seminar she sat alone, convinced her fellow students could sense her 'stupidity' and did not want to be associated with her.

Everyone else looked so confident and seemed to have friends. When anyone smiled at her, she was convinced it was because they were laughing at her, or feeling sorry for her. She remembered other times in class or at her accommodation when she felt alone and isolated, and she began to build a story in her head about how much others didn't like her. She then found herself going over the conversation she had had with her mum the previous night.

Ten minutes into the seminar she realised she had not heard a word the lecturer had been saying ... she was on autopilot.

Explanation: Automatic pilot

Automatic pilot is a common feeling, described by Williams and Penman (2010) as the mind being in one place while the body is somewhere else. It's a state of constantly *doing*, not *being*. This state of *doing* often means that we miss the small positives in our daily lives. There are lots of ways of being on autopilot; for example, you may be getting on a bus and showing your ticket, but actually thinking about a conversation you had with a housemate the day before, or you might be riding your bike to university while idly thinking about the plans you have for going out later. We have all experienced going into a room purpose-fully and then forgetting why we had done so, or sitting down in the library and forgetting which assignment we planned to focus on. Williams and Penman (2010) assert that we can only truly focus on one thing at a time (and yes, that includes so-called multi-taskers!). They also say that if we are overloaded with thoughts and worries our working memories start to malfunction, which makes us indecisive, powerless, unaware of our surroundings, forgetful, exhausted and stressed. They give the analogy of a computer with too many windows and programmes open. After some time, the computer will run more slowly and less efficiently and eventually it will crash, much like a human being who is over-loaded.

Think of the times you have sat down to read an article or a chapter, but got distracted by your social media feed. Maybe you followed links to interesting but irrelevant information on current events and then closed your computer before realising you hadn't read the article you planned to. This is a common experience when you are overloaded and not focusing on the moment. It can undermine your work and leave you feeling frustrated and apprehensive.

Practice: Bringing awareness

The practice for the first week is an exercise which helps bring awareness to an everyday action. The Raisin Meditation, which is well known by people familiar with mindfulness, involves the act of eating a raisin, but in a mindful, fully aware way. The main aspects of the Raisin Meditation are recognising how quickly we go into automatic pilot, how we are constantly doing rather than being and just acknowledging the experience of being in the moment and being curious. In fact, cultivating a sense of curiosity is central to mindfulness. This is a human quality celebrated by Eleanor Roosevelt, who said:

> *"Life was meant to be lived, and curiosity must be kept alive. One must never, for whatever reason, turn her back on life."*

There are six key aims of the Raisin Meditation:

1 It is experiential so it teaches you to tune into your experiences moment by moment.

2 It introduces the concept of autopilot; eating is something we usually do without needing to think very much, so the focus on all of the senses whilst eating teaches you to be present.

3 The exercise embodies curiosity; which is a core principle of mindfulness; becoming curious about eating a raisin can show you that you can bring curiosity to all aspects of your life.

4 Because eating a raisin is such an everyday activity, the exercise shows that meditation is not mystical. Mindfulness meditation can be about the ordinary, everyday experiences that we all have.

5 The exercise employs all of the senses, which is another core element of mindfulness. It makes connections between physical experiences and emotional reactions; eating is a physical act, but it is often laden with strong emotions.

6 Because we are in a constant state of doing, when we stop and explore a raisin for example, we discover all sorts of things bringing curiosity and non-judgement.

You only need to set aside 5–10 minutes to do the raisin exercise. So, make sure you won't get disturbed by friends or family or your phone so you can concentrate fully. You will need some raisins, together with a piece of paper and a pen to write down your feelings and reactions. You will be eating the raisins in a mindful way, taking at least 20 seconds on each of the following stages, and then afterwards putting your pen to paper. (Note, a raisin is traditionally used in this exercise, but this can be substituted for other food or drinks such as a glass of water or a piece of chocolate.) You can try this exercise with a food that is familiar to you such as an avocado, a mango, some pomegranate seeds – whatever you fancy. Learning the raisin exercise increases mindfulness, helps overcome autopilot and develops curiosity in everyday activities. A step-by-step guide on how to do the raisin exercise is included in the teaching notes for this chapter.

The raisin exercise teaches you to focus on the moment and on what you are doing in the moment. By focusing on a small act such as eating a raisin, you are allowing yourself to really experience being in the moment. When you do the raisin exercise, you may realise that you spend a lot of your time thinking about other things rather than focusing on what you are actually doing in the moment. However, mindfulness is not about *controlling* the chattering mind, but about noticing when your thoughts are trying to take you away from your focus and choosing not to follow those thoughts. In a way, this gives you the freedom to engage, so mindfulness practice gives you the ability to choose how you react. Regular mindfulness practice trains the mind to focus and helps us to dissolve habits that drive routine behaviour.

When you first try mindfulness meditation, you may feel frustrated by it. At first your mind might wander all over the place and you may feel that you are not good at meditating. It can be easy to give up and listen to your inner critic; however, if you persist, after a few tries you may realise that you can begin to focus on your breathing and 'see' your thoughts – in a strange way this helps us to let go of them. This is an important aspect of mindfulness, because although we don't have control over our thoughts, we do have choices about how we think about our thoughts and how we relate to them. You will need to set aside time each day to practise mindfulness.

It is important to try to be kind to yourself and to acknowledge the 'babbling mind'. As you practise mindfulness, thoughts will come up and distract you from your breath, but try to kindly usher the thoughts away. Some people find it helpful to imagine their mind as the sky and their thoughts as clouds that move across the sky. Try to focus on keeping the 'sky' constant and try not to give your attention to the 'clouds' that are passing through. It can be very useful just to acknowledge the thoughts you are having. For example, you might say to yourself, 'Ah, this is a planning thought, or a worry thought or a thought about what's for dinner'. This practice of focusing and acknowledging thoughts as they arise is incredibly useful when studying. Often when reading a book, we get to the end of a page and realise that we haven't actually taken in the contents of the text, but instead our mind has wandered off elsewhere. This practice of focusing on small acts such as eating can, once mastered, be transferred to study habits.

Letting go of habits

Letting go of habits is a good way to be more mindful of the moment and to focus on what you are doing. For example, you might try changing where you sit to study or the times at which you study. This may enable you to be more 'in the moment' in your new space or time. Many of our habits are ingrained, so we feel that it is impossible to change them. For example, perhaps you never make time for breakfast in the morning before class because you are always running late. However, you could set your alarm a little earlier to enable you to wake up more gradually. You can allow time to wash and have a cup of tea before you have to leave the house for class. This will enable you to feel more positive about your classes, which will have a positive effect on your interaction with other students. You can also experiment with sitting near to other students and engaging in small talk before class. This might help you to realise that there are things that you have in common and not everyone is already in a fixed group of friends. So, over time you can make connections with other students, which will have a positive impact on your study habits because you might find that you actually want to go to the library after class to study with your friends from the course. This example illustrates that the one small habit release of allowing time to wake up earlier can have a positive impact on many other experiences and perceptions of life.

Meditation: Body and Breath

This is a short meditation to help you to focus on this moment. As you settle for this meditation, it is important to try and take on the attitude of kindness and tenderness towards yourself, so sit on a chair or lie down in as comfortable but alert position as possible. If you are sitting on a chair, have your back erect but not standing to attention and make sure that the soles of your feet are touching the ground and your legs are uncrossed. If you are lying down, have your feet uncrossed and your hands by your sides. Close your eyes if this is comfortable for you, or have a soft, lowered gaze.

Now, gently bring your attention to all the places in your body where you can feel the contact your body has with the surface which is supporting you. If you are lying down, perhaps you can feel your back touching the mat or your bed. If you are sitting on a chair, perhaps you can feel your buttocks and thighs as they are held by the chair or your back against the chair.

Now, move your attention like the beam of a torch to the soles of both feet, the toes, the ankles. Tune into any sensations you feel; warmth or cold, throbbing or fidgeting. Or perhaps you feel nothing at all – that is absolutely fine too. You are not trying to create sensations, just try to gently notice whatever is already there.

Next, move your awareness up the lower legs to the knees and thighs, simply noticing what you feel or don't feel along the way. You may soon notice that your mind is no longer with your legs but has wandered off down a familiar old pathway drifting towards thoughts of the past or the future, worries or daydreams. Don't worry if this happens, it's normal and does not mean you are doing anything wrong, it's just what the mind does. Your task is just to notice when the mind has wandered and, as best you can, escort your attention back to wherever you are. Each time you notice the mind has wandered, call it back. This is mindfulness practice.

Now, gently take your awareness to your back and shoulders, noticing if they are hunched forward or tight. Then move your focus all the way down your arms to your fingertips. Are there any sensations here or in the palm of your hands? Move your attention up through your neck to your face and head. Is your jaw tight? Could you loosen it a little in a kind and attentive way? Just check in with your whole body.

Now, gather up your attention and purposely take it to the places in your body where you can feel the sensations of your breath. Perhaps you feel your breath most strongly in your tummy. If comfortable, put the palm of your hand gently on your tummy or chest where you can feel the movement of the inbreath gently expanding your tummy towards your hand and the outbreath as the tummy or chest retreats a little. For others you may feel the cool inbreath filled with oxygen as it enters through the nostrils and the warmth of the outbreath as you exhale.

You can exaggerate this feeling if you need to anchor yourself more deeply in connection with your breath. Take a deep breath in and feel the flow of the cool air moving through your nose, down your windpipe and the openings of your lungs, and then a long slow outbreath as you feel the warm breath leaving your body.

Finally, just for a couple of minutes allow the breath to find its own natural rhythm and just follow your breath in this moment. When the mind wanders, and it inevitably will, give yourself a pat on the back each time you notice.

You are not trying to have an empty mind, this is almost impossible for humans, but you are trying to gain some control over when and where it wanders to give yourself more agency.

So, just focus on your breath or your body as best you can and gently allow your attention to expand away from the breath to the whole of the body sitting or lying and prepare to come to the end of this meditation. Gently twiddle your fingers and toes, have a gentle stretch or yawn and, in your own time, open your eyes as you come back into an everyday awareness of yourself and your surroundings.

Reflection: Three systems – threat, drive, soothe

After this meditation you may notice that it is not that easy to keep your mind focused on the breath. This is natural because minds are developed to wander. However, in this exercise, you are working to manage the wandering mind. Each time a thought comes along, perhaps you can visualise the thought like a cloud, and on the front of the cloud is the name of the thought that is trying to take you away. The thought might be a worry, or a plan, or 'what if' or 'if only …'.' – or even, how long is this going to last? As soon as you notice these thoughts, see if you can name the thought, and see if you can let that cloud pass and focus on the constant presence of the sky. Then come back to being with the breath and being aware of the breath, in whatever way is best for you.

Try following the breath, gently … perhaps noticing when the inbreath is complete and when the outbreath begins. Or place one hand on your heart and one hand on your belly and feel the rise and fall of your body. If your mind wanders, remember there is nothing wrong with this, but as soon as you notice, congratulate yourself for noticing and, kindly but firmly, bring your attention back to your breathing.

Some of our basic brain structures have not changed since the time of our cave dweller ancestors. At this time, existence was driven by basic needs of survival. The brain needed a bias towards warding off physical threats, hunting for food and restoring through rest. We need to have a balance of the three systems of threat to protect ourselves:

- to eat
- to find shelter and reproduce
- to soothe to regulate back to our full mental and physical strength.

For anyone who has watched wildlife programmes or watched their own pets at home, we know that animals spend far more time in the soothing mode than either of the other two modes.

Gilbert (2013) believes distress is a result of an imbalance of the three systems in our society with a heavy deficit in the soothing system. Gilbert developed this theory in the context of modern life, where many of us are not at risk from external physical threats, but we are at high risk of internal emotional turmoil. He proposes that human beings need to switch between three main systems in order to manage their emotions. Gilbert says that each system (feeding, sheltering and soothing) is connected with a different part of the brain, and this creates different brain chemistry. The soothing system is what we are working to activate in mindfulness as we move from the constant doing into a state of being. Table 1 is based on Gilbert's work (2013) and shows how the three different systems work.

Table 1: Applying doing, versus being, to students' experience (based on Gilbert, 2013)

System	Purpose	Explanation	Application
Threat system: for example, a cat running from a dog	The purpose is threat detection and protection	When the threat system is turned on, it pumps out adrenaline and cortisol, and brings up feelings such as anger, anxiety and depression. This leads to the Fight, Flight or Freeze response, which can lead to panic attacks and prevent us from taking in and absorbing learning or focusing on anything else apart from our stress	Germer (2009) has identified our modern-day stress response, which is not about actual life-threatening danger but will be familiar behaviour to many students: **Fight:** constant self-criticism **Flight:** isolating self away from others **Freeze:** over-identifying with rigid ideas that we have about ourselves or the world, which could lead to ruminating
Drive system: for example, a cat hunting a mouse	The purpose of the drive system is to trigger our survival instinct. It also motivates us to get the things we want and it drives us to seek short-term rewards. It can also produce feelings of comparison and competition	It pumps out the hormone dopamine, which is the brain's communication system. This sends messages to the body such as: wanting, pursuing, perfectionism, achieving and progressing	These are common feelings among students and in many ways academic study creates an environment where these conditions are in-built in the structure of the curriculum and the assessment framework

(continued)

Table 1: (*Continued*).

System	Purpose	Explanation	Application
Soothing system: for example, a cat lying in the sun or on a radiator	The purpose of the soothing system is to regulate distress and to activate the parasympathetic nervous system, which helps the body relax and gives us time to digest food, to nourish our bodies and rest our mind and emotions	It pumps out the hormone oxytocin, opiates and serotonin, which are the hormones and chemicals associated with love, bonding, wellbeing and happiness. They produce feelings of warmth, connection, contentment, safety and trust	Students who leave home to go to university, or who travel overseas for study, are far from their familiar soothing systems. The intersectionality of difference can compound these feelings in environments where the self is not reflected in others. This can cause distress until the student has established new soothing habits to de-stress

Threat

Students have 'threats' which are not only experienced within studies, but socially and in shared accommodation. Although all these aspects of students' experience may be fine, for many they are a source of threat. This means that the mind is constantly swaying between the 'threat' and 'drive' system, where even the things that are meant to be restful and rejuvenating become another source of *doing*. Of course, sometimes the threat and drive systems are necessary to do well in life. However, without the constitutional repair of the soothing system, the threat will not work well to motivate and drive activity. This is because it gets turned on permanently so you interpret everything, even your own thoughts, as a threat. This infuses the system with adrenaline and cortisol, which in turn makes it very difficult to settle, study, learn or write, or to trust in your abilities to rest, digest or feel confident with others.

Drive

The same is true of the drive system. We need it to get on in life and motivate ourselves to work, but without soothing the drive becomes a constant need to achieve, work hard and be the best. It leads to feelings of jealousy of others' success or competitiveness. This can lead to constantly seeking material rewards or affirmation of popularity or attraction, which might be doubly difficult to achieve if you are seen as different from your peers, because of, for example; race, colour, language, gender identity, neurodiversity, disability, sexuality or class.

Soothe

When we are bombarded with so much *doing* to avoid threat or to achieve, we leave little time to allow ourselves to rest and just be. Therefore, we need to work at just *being*. This means resting the brain without being hijacked by thoughts of the future or the past. It involves just practising being right here, right now. This nourishes the nervous system and brain so that the next time you need to spring into action and focus, you have the best of your capacities available. *Being* is what we need to rest and recuperate. This is what mindfulness is, but it takes practice just to be and not be *bullied* by the constant chatter of thoughts. The brain is a great faculty that we have as human beings, but to make it work the best and clearest and wisest for us, we need to service it and give it time off. It is the only organ in the body that does not sleep, so we have to make sure we give it some down time.

Just like eating the raisin, we will be trying to really focus on our lives, studies and experiences as they are in the moment. The ingredients we need for that are:

1 To develop the muscle of attention to keep focused.
2 To watch our wandering thoughts and do the best we can whilst endeavouring to name our thoughts, but not follow them.
3 To bring an attitude of absolute kindness and compassion to ourselves. There is no way to get this wrong so we have no reason to be hard on ourselves. We need to cultivate an inner best friend to support us.
4 To be patient and not strive to be relaxed, just try to notice, and most of all try to be accepting and non-judgemental of ourselves. Then we can begin our journey to enter into the rejuvenating world of the soothing system so that when needed we can be a productive, wise and fulfilled person. Therefore, when we need the drive or threat system, they are refreshed and work efficiently for us.

Lesson Plan: Session 1
Session aim: Introduce participants to the main principles of mindfulness and set the atmosphere for the 5-week course
Objectives: 1. Participants begin to get to know each other 2. Participants agree on a 'goodwill contract' for the sessions 3. Use the breath to anchor mindfulness 4. Group practices; bringing awareness to an everyday activity.

Activities:	Time:
1. **Ice breaker activity:** In pairs or groups of three, participants introduce themselves and find out things they have in common. Briefly introduce students to what mindfulness is and how the course is structured.	15 minutes
2. **Goodwill contract:** Identify the four key principles of the contract: Confidentiality, Compassion, Listening and Respect. Students discuss and agree on definitions of these four principles.	15 minutes
3. **Meditation:** Body and Breath Meditation (see script).	10 minutes
4. **Raisin exercise:** Each participant takes a raisin and follows the guidance of the group leader.	15 minutes
5. **Enquiry:** Invite group to share their experiences: ○ *What did you notice?* ○ *What did you feel in your body?* ○ *What happened afterwards?* ○ *Did anyone else experience the same, or something different?*	20 minutes
6. **Autopilot:** Students identify one autopilot habit they would like to change.	10 minutes

Notes:

1. If you are working online, the ice breaker activity can be done using breakout rooms.
2. The group leader will need to note the discussion and write up the goodwill contract for circulation after the session. It is very important that all participants in a mindfulness group feel comfortable and supported, not just by the group leader, but also by the other members of the group, so time spent at the beginning setting that atmosphere will pay off as the course develops.
3. This meditation is about coming to the breath. Ask students to find their seat, FOFBOC (feet on floor, bum on chair). Tell them to make sure that their back is self-supporting (head over heart, heart over pelvis), or they can imagine a piece of string all the way through the body and coming out of the top of their heads. Next, tell students to keep their eyes closed or try to have a soft, downward gaze so that they can focus on coming to the breath.
4. The group leader will read the script below (you could use other foods/drinks, e.g. water/other fruits, etc.)
5. At the enquiry stage it is important that students feel that they can share their experiences freely and without judgement. Each time a participant shares something, praise them for 'good noticing'.
6. After the raisin exercise, students choose one routine habit in their daily life and make a deliberate effort to change it. This might be a waking up habit, where you sit in class or what you do when you get home after class. Try to introduce a change in your habit. This will enable you to focus on it and notice how you feel when you change things. This can sometimes bring up feelings of discomfort or irritation, but it will also allow you to be more conscious of your autopilot.

> **Homework:**
> Below are some strategies which may be able to help you, by offering them to the participants:
> - Listen to the mindfulness of breath from an online site such as Headspace.
> - Try to do one routine activity mindfully daily and record it in the form below; (see page 23); eg; eating something, brushing your teeth, drinking the first nice drink of the day, showering, two minutes walking. The important thing, whilst doing the activity, is to try to keep the 'thought clouds' at bay.

Example of a goodwill contract

- **Confidentiality:** Do not share others' stories, and do not take others' stories outside of the group. However, it is okay to share any of the mindfulness material and your own experiences if you want to.
- **Self-kindness:** It is okay to make a mistake; mindfulness is not about getting it right the first time. This may also be an opportunity to start to notice when you are unkind to yourself.
- **Listen:** Within mindfulness sessions, topics might arise which are normally difficult to discuss. Within this context, group members and even the group leader might inadvertently cause offence; try to listen to participants' points of view and respect diversity in the group.
- **Respect:** 'Calling in' rather than 'calling out'. This means that if a person in the group says something which another member of the group finds offensive or difficult, perhaps because they perceive it as discriminatory, rather than label it as racist/sexist/homophobic, etc., try to say, 'when you say that, I feel that you are ignoring my experiences of …'. This enables you to find your voice and own your experience and perhaps the student who has inadvertently caused offence to hear the impact of their words in a non-confrontational way.

Facilitating a meditation

- Be aware of the possibility of someone struggling during the session and recognise some of the signs and symptoms of trauma reaction.
- If you notice distress or discomfort, respond in a way that soothes rather than exacerbates. In our experience, this is best done by being as permissive as possible when leading the session, giving participants choice and encouraging them to make choices.
- During the meditation, it is useful to keep your eyes open or open them periodically, to support physical, emotional and psychological safety in the group.
- Check to see if anyone looks uncomfortable or distressed, make eye contact with them so they do not feel alone, and weave into the meditation reminders of how to ground ourselves. Further information on this can be found on Treleaven's website (link in the references section below).
- Try to remember to reiterate at the beginning of each meditation how important it is that participants only follow our instructions if they are comfortable doing so and that they listen to themselves in this respect. Remind them of the

choices they have, such as their posture and the ways in which they can anchor and ground themselves if they feel uncomfortable or overwhelmed.
- Give alternatives to focusing on the breath.

Raisin exercise script

- **Holding and seeing:** Take one of your raisins or pieces of fruit, place it in your hand, or between your fingers and thumb. Really concentrate on it, as if you have never seen it before; experience more closely its shape, its weight and whether it casts a shadow. Let your eyes explore every detail: the highlights where the light hits it, the nooks and crannies – take your time.
- **Touching:** Now roll the raisin about in the palm of your hand, and also roll it between your fingers; really explore its texture, changing hands if you want.
- **Smelling:** Now put it under your nose. What do you notice each time you inhale? Does it have a noticeable smell, or nothing at all? Whatever the result, be aware.
- **Placing it in the mouth:** Now lift your hand with the raisin towards your mouth; notice the bending of your arm to your mouth, and be aware of how your arm knows what to do. Now place it in the mouth, noticing how your tongue knows how to accept this gift; roll it around your mouth, but don't chew, just explore for about 30 seconds.
- **Chewing:** When you feel ready, start to chew. Consciously notice the effects of chewing; notice the raisin's taste, notice its texture on your teeth as you bite into it. Continue to chew for a while, and be very aware of everything in your mouth, but don't swallow yet.
- **Swallow:** Notice the first signs that you want to swallow as it crops up in your mind, before the raisin is actually swallowed. Notice how it feels in your mouth, and how the tongue prepares too; follow the sensations. As you then swallow the raisin, consciously feel as it goes down to your stomach; if it takes you longer to swallow, two or three attempts, notice this.
- **After-effects:** After you have swallowed, notice how your tongue feels and what sensations are left over in your mouth. Is there an aftertaste? Do you feel the urge to eat another raisin? What does it feel like now that the raisin has gone?

Learning points from the raisin exercise

- **Awareness of and interrupting your autopilot:** especially with the senses – sight, touch, sound, smell, taste – which evoke memories and shift mood.
- **Awareness of being versus doing:** usually we just eat and think about something else, rather than experiencing and being fully present.
- **Knowledge that the mind will wander:** it will tell you stories and remind you of memories about the raisin, always comparing and judging. That is okay as long as you are aware of these thoughts. If the memories are good or

bad, they may affect your mood. If this happens with a raisin, it is useful to reflect on what happens in the mind when you are trying to study or revise.

- **Understand what gets in the way when trying to focus:** for example, social media, random websites, negative or self-sabotaging thoughts. Think about what you need to do to anchor your thoughts when your mind has gone off. For example, you may focus on breath, count beads, or recite a phrase or song.

Choices for listening to your breath

Some students may find focusing on their breath difficult. Below are some strategies which can help.

- Just listen and notice your breath as you breathe in and out
- Visualisation: imagine breathing in and out like the waves of the sea
- If you struggle to listen or visualise, count your breath as you breathe in and start the count again as you breathe out; take slightly longer breaths in and out
- If you want to, you can combine the breath with body movements, so open and close your hands in time with your breath
- If you still have trouble with the above, then you can focus on your feet instead, really feeling your feet planted on the floor.

Daily practice diary

Day	Practice (Yes/No)	Comments: what did you notice?
Monday		
Tuesday		
Wednesday		
Thursday		
Friday		
Saturday		
Sunday		

Resources

There are many books on mindfulness. The ones below are recommended starting points.

Frankel, V. (2004) *Man's Search for Meaning: The Classic Tribute to Hope from the Holocaust*. London: Penguin.

Kabat-Zinn, J. (2013) *Full Catastrophe Living: Using the Wisdom of Your Body and Mind to Face Stress, Pain, and Illness*. New York: Bantam Dell.

King, R. (2018) *Mindful of Race: Understanding and Transforming Habits of Harm: Transforming Racism from the Inside*. Boulder, CA: Sounds True.

McGilchrist, I. (2012) *The Master and His Emissary: The Divided Brain and the Making of the Western World*. New Haven, CT: Yale University Press.

Menakem, R. (2021) *My Grandmother's Hands: Racialized Trauma and the Pathway to Mending Our Hearts and Bodies*. London: Penguin.

Oliver, M. (2004) *Wild Geese: Selected Poems*. Hexham: Bloodaxe Books.

Remen, R. (2006) *Kitchen Table Wisdom: Stories that Heal*. London: Penguin.

Rumi, J. (1995) *The Essential Rumi*, trans. C. Barks. San Francisco, CA: Harper.

Santorelli, S. (2000) *Heal Thy Self: Lessons on Mindfulness in Medicine*. New York: Bell Tower.

Williams, M. and Penman, D. (2010) *Mindfulness: A Practical Guide to Finding Peace in a Frantic World*. London: Piatkus Books.

References

Germer, C. (2009) *The Mindful Path to Self-Compassion*. New York: Guilford Press.

Gilbert, P. (2013) *The Compassionate Mind*, 3rd edition. London: Constable & Robinson.

Treleaven, D. (n.d.) https://davidtreleaven.com/ [accessed 27 May 2022].

Williams, M. and Penman, D. (2010) *Mindfulness: A Practical Guide to Finding Peace in a Frantic World*. London: Piatkus Books.

2 Living in your head

Olu's story

Olu checked her WhatsApp messages again. She had messaged the girl she had met last night but hadn't received an immediate reply, so she turned off her phone and went to sleep. This morning the first thing she did after she woke up was check her phone again, but there was no message. She could see that the message had been read and the girl had been online because Olu could see she had liked a couple of things on Instagram. Later in the library Olu started to worry about why she hadn't messaged. Olu thought, 'oh, it's because she doesn't really like me, we just had a kiss in a club and a follow-up date at a café bar, she's not really interested in me'.

Later that day Olu met up with her friends Ed and Ali. Ed asked her what was up, so she told him that the girl that she met last week in a club hadn't returned her message from last night. Ed told Olu not to worry about it, the girl might have lost her phone. Ali suggested that the girl's phone may have been out of charge or she might not have had a signal. This did not help Olu, because she felt sure that this wasn't why she hadn't received a message.

Then Olu thought, maybe the girl is straight and the kiss had been a mistake. It felt like there had been a connection, but maybe Olu was wrong and the girl was just drunk and being friendly. That night back at her house, Olu thought perhaps the girl was just busy and had forgotten to reply, but again this didn't help.

Later that evening Olu phoned her sister and told her she was feeling down. After explaining things, Olu's sister laughed and told her that the girl sounded normal and that Olu was the one being weird, expecting immediate replies from a girl she had only met twice. This made Olu feel worse as she knew that there was a connection between them.

After moping about the house for an hour or so, Olu decided to go out to her Tae Kwon Do class. She changed into her sports gear and met her friend at the gym. After an hour of defensive kicks, blocks and some shadowing practice, she felt much better and she decided to go for a drink with her friend. On the way home they stopped for noodles at her favourite take-out and bumped into a couple of people from her course. After chatting with them, she got home late. After having had a shower, she finally got into bed and checked her phone. There were two messages waiting for her on WhatsApp from the girl from the club!

"Hey! Thanks for your message. Soz for late reply, I was cooking when I read your message and then I totally forgot to reply."

"Are you around tomorrow night for a drink?"

Olu had a large grin on her face, she waited a couple minutes and then replied.

Explanation: Living in our heads

This story reminds us that sometimes the world is not how it is, it is how we think it is. Which means that if we practise, we can learn not to react to unsettling thoughts. This can be a particularly difficult lesson for students to learn because at university they are constantly rewarded and encouraged to *live in their heads*. University study places a premium on skills of analysis and students are trained to increase their capacity for critical thinking. However, although this is an invaluable intellectual skill, it may not be so useful when applied to your emotional life.

In the story, Olu knows that she is prone to lack confidence in relationships. She always needs a lot of reassurance when she meets someone new and she is likely to think the worst if left to her own thoughts for too long. However, mindfulness practice reminds us that thoughts are not facts and that although we cannot control negative thoughts, we can control how we respond to them. Looking back on the scenario, Olu realised that going to Tae Kwon Do had been the right thing to do. It had taken her thoughts from going over and over her WhatsApp messages and instead allowed her to focus on a physical activity. This is also what mindfulness teaches us to do, so that even without a diverting activity such as Tae Kwon Do, we can learn to control our reactions to negative thoughts. This enables us to cultivate a *compassionate friend* (Gilbert, 2013) in our minds, so that when we start to feel negative reactions, our compassionate friend voice can help to settle our mind and allow us to choose how we want to respond.

This does not mean that we allow people to take advantage of us, or treat us badly, but that we make an active choice of when to ignite our negative reactions allowing us to make a wise choice. We can choose which path to follow. It is almost as if we can watch our thoughts as they go through our minds. This way of thinking develops the Buddhist practice of '*Metta*', which translates to loving kindness towards ourselves and others.

Practice: The body scan

The meditation practice for this week is the body scan. It was introduced by Jon Kabat-Zinn to the 8 week Mindfulness Based Stress Reduction (MBSR) course as an adaptation of a meditation learnt from Zen meditation and yoga practice. The MBSR course was originally designed for patients in a hospital setting with chronic medical conditions. In these contexts, it was not practical or compassionate to ask them to sit in a traditional non-moving meditation position, nor was it meant as a purely relaxation pose. Thus, the body scan invites participants to 'fall fully awake' to have a direct experience of the body.

The body scan can have a beneficial quality of relaxation but this is not the aim. The aim of it is to 'tune in' to the differing, shifting sensations in the body to gather information. The body scan uses the attitudinal foundation of non-striving, which is useful because, often the moment we are told to relax, our bodies can tense up more than ever. Moreover, relaxation can be an almost impossible task for people whose bodies have carried years of tension and stress. Therefore, in the body scan, we try to be with whatever experience we have. This means focusing on feeling just how you are without having a specific goal. The body scan allows you to bring compassionate non-judgemental awareness to what you find. It focuses on systematically moving your attention through the body, tuning in to the sensations picked up from different parts of the body. The aim is to separate these sensations from your thoughts about them or your reactions to them. This allows you to focus and then let go before refocusing on another area of the body.

Meditation: Body Scan

Settle: Sit in a comfortable place and fully relax your body. You do not need to be lying down, but it helps, particularly if you are doing a Body Scan Meditation before you fall asleep. Try to get into a position that is comfortable enough for you to fully relax without becoming so comfortable that you may fall asleep, especially if you're not able to nap or sleep at the moment. Let your breathing slow down, and start breathing from your belly instead of from your chest, letting your abdomen expand and contract with each breath. If you find your shoulders rising and falling with each breath, focus more on breathing from your belly, as though it is a balloon inflating and deflating in your abdomen with each breath.

Notice where tension lies: Starting with your head, bring your awareness to your body and notice any tension you are feeling as you practise your Body Scan Meditation. Try to breathe into your head, allowing your breath to fill your head and smooth any tension. If you are frowning or your jaw is tight, try to breathe into those places and allow your breath to relax you.

Start anchoring your attention by tuning in to all the places where you can feel contact with the surface below you. Maybe this is your head resting against the floor or the chair, or the feeling of the surface below your buttocks and your legs. Then, gently, move your attention as if taking a spotlight with you, to the area of your breath. So, tune in to all the places where you can feel your breath entering, and exiting, your body most vividly. Perhaps you can put your hands on your tummy, and feel the rise and fall of your breath, like the waves of the sea. Each inbreath moves your diaphragm or tummy towards the palms of your hands. Each outbreath releases and moves your tummy away from your hands. If your mind wanders, try not to judge yourself – it's not wrong, it's just what minds do. But, as soon as you can, with kindness and firmness, see if you can bring your attention back to your breath. Then move the spotlight of your attention all the way down to your toes in both feet, and see if you can notice anything here: the feel of your socks, or shoes, or blanket.

Then move your attention to take in the whole of both your feet and notice if they feel warm or cold. Or, perhaps you don't feel anything. That's fine too. Now, allow the feet to dissolve from being the focus of your awareness and take the spotlight of your awareness to move up your lower legs, noticing if there's any tightness in your calf muscles. Then move to the area of your knees and take your attention all the way up your thighs. Are you holding on tight here? Can you feel your clothing around your thighs? Or, perhaps you can feel the floor or the chair below you? Now, once again, move the spotlight of your attention to the area of your buttocks and the pelvic region. Notice if there are any sensations in your pelvic region. Notice if there's any tightness in the organs in this part of your body. Are there any feelings of fullness, bloating or cramping? And now, expand the spotlight of your awareness to imagine that you can take a deep breath in, and that breath can move all the way through the bottom half of your body, through your pelvic region, down your legs, feet and toes, refreshing and renewing every cell in the lower half of your body. Then, on the outbreath, release and let go of every cell from this part of your body.

If your mind wanders, try not to judge yourself, your mind or your thoughts, but perhaps you can notice the thought and name it. It is a thought that is trying to whisk you away, so as best you can, and as quickly as you can, with kindness, escort your attention back to being with your lower back. The lower back can be an area that can be tense or cause discomfort. Notice if this is true for you, or if another part of your body is calling you with discomfort or tension. You can always choose to shift your position mindfully, moving your body in a way that makes it more comfortable. Or, if you discover something like an itch, or a small intensity, or a restlessness, you can just be curious about it, and see what happens to the intensity if you just, gently, notice the shape or the rhythm of it. Sometimes, we brace against and intensify tension. If this happens for you, you can always breathe into the area of tension, and on the outbreath, release, letting go of any unnecessary bracing. Or, you can come back to the anchor of your breath, if the tension is taking away your focus.

Now, move your attention from the lower back, all the way up the spine and the sides of your back. All the way up the ribcage to the shoulder blades, the shoulders, noticing what you are feeling here. Gently move down each arm, noticing any tightness, or clenching, and sensations in the fingertips. Then, bring your attention to the front of your torso: the breasts or the pecs, the lungs. Notice if you can feel them as they move with the in and the outbreath. Now move your attention all the way down, to the area of the belly. Notice if your belly feels soft and comfortable or tight and full; just notice without judgement.

If your mind starts to get involved, gently, but firmly, see if you can escort it all the way up to the neck and the throat. Take in the back of your head, and any sensations in the scalp, to the top of the head and your forehead – is it carrying a frown? Now move to your eyes, do they feel heavy, or ready to open? Just notice any sensations in your nose, your ears, your mouth, your jaw. Now, expand the spotlight of your awareness again, and imagine that you can send the breath, like a beam of a torch, to refresh and renew every cell in your head, face, neck and torso in the inbreath, and release from every cell from your head, face and neck on the outbreath.

As we finish the body scan, take a deep breath in, and imagine that without having to control it, you can trust the breath to move from the top of your head to the tip of your toes, refreshing and renewing, releasing and letting go. As you come to the end of the body scan, and you prepare to bring yourself back to your everyday consciousness and thoughts, congratulate yourself for having taken the time to do this exercise, knowing that in doing this you are actively taking a part in your own wellbeing and developing the muscle of attention, so that you, little by little, are gaining some control over your thoughts and the ones which you choose to follow.

To end the Body Scan Meditation: Spend the last minute of the body scan just breathing in a deep but relaxed way and allow your mind to focus on whichever part of the body it wants to. When you are ready, slowly start to re-awaken your body by gently moving your fingers and toes and limbs, opening your eyes and when you are ready sit up.

Final notes on the body scan: Practise the Body Scan Meditation anytime you feel stress or once a day. If you do not have a lot of time, you can do a quicker version of this Body Scan Meditation by just sitting and noticing any place in your body that you are carrying tension, rather than moving area by area. This will become easier as you practise the meditation regularly. This meditation can promote body awareness, stress awareness and relaxation, so try to practise it often. You can also try progressive muscle relaxation exercises, breathing exercises or visualisation exercises for releasing stress and tension in your body.

Tips for the body scan

1 Regardless of what happens (for example, if you fall asleep, lose concentration, keep thinking of other things, focusing on the wrong bit of your body or not feeling anything), just do it! These are your experiences in the moment. Just be aware of them.

2 If your mind is wandering a lot, simply note the thoughts (as passing events) and then bring the mind gently back to the body scan.

3 Let go of ideas of 'success', 'failure', 'doing it really well' or 'trying to purify the body'. This is not a competition. It is not a skill for which you need to strive. The only discipline involved is regular and frequent practice. Just do it with an attitude of openness and curiosity.

4 Let go of any expectations about what the body scan will do for you – imagine it as a seed you have planted. The more you poke around and interfere, the less it will be able to develop. So, with the body scan, just give it the right conditions – peace and quiet, and regular and frequent practice.

5 Try approaching your experience in each moment with an attitude of acceptance of the way things are. If you try to fight off unpleasant thoughts, feelings or body sensations, the upsetting feelings will only distract you from doing anything else. Therefore, you need to try to be aware, be non-striving, be in the moment, and accept things as they are.

Reflection: Functions of the body scan are multi-layered

The body scan focuses the muscle of awareness and attention, which develops your neural pathways for sustained concentration. As you do this, you become increasingly familiar with the disruptions of the chattering mind. The body scan gives you practice of noticing where your thoughts, feelings and impulses take you and allows you to have some control and choice over whether you follow them or not. As you develop this skill, you can 'watch' where your mind or emotions wander without being submerged by them.

Neuroscience, which looks at the activity of the mind, has made a surprising observation; when the mind is involved in a cognitive task, certain parts of the brain activity decrease whilst the areas involved in the task are active. When the task is complete, rather than there being a pause in neural activity, there is an increase. Therefore, it seems the brain is never willingly at rest. Even when we are not pursuing a particular task, the brain is working, mulling over all the information we have put into it and it seems to have a tendency to ruminate over thoughts to do with our sense of self, such as: how we are perceived by others, what we have said, whether we have been wronged and so on. This is a kind of obsessive thinking which was originally intended to protect us but actually often leads to intense periods of rumination. It can lead to some very unhealthy self-critical thoughts, which can include negative moods, emotional upset, anxiety and even depression. However, research from the University of California has revealed that simple meditation habits of focusing our attention can help us develop 'cognitive control'. This is a useful skill for students for three reasons. First, because it helps you to develop concentration, improve your working memory, and it can increase scores in tests. In a study by Saron (2013), students reported that regular mindfulness attention training helped their ability to manage their impulses and distractions. This cognitive control is thought to be linked to improved emotional wellbeing and less rumination. Second, it helps to develop the attitudes of kindness, patience and curiosity. This can help cultivate a pathway to challenge judgemental thinking, thus bringing compassion to the self. So, by introducing a language of tenderness and non-judgement to the body, you can build a sense of acceptance for what you find. This enables you to attend to discomfort or tension with kindness rather than intensifying the discomfort by bracing against it or condemning and hating it. So, instead of being defensive, you are promoting a sense of curiosity directed at soothing and helping. Third, the body scan gives you an opportunity to develop a new more direct relationship with your body. Goleman and Davidson (2017: 89) illustrate this with an example:

> "If you give the back of your hand a hard pinch, different brain systems mobilise, some for the pure sensation of pain, and others for our dislike of that pain. The brain unifies them into a visceral, instant Ouch!"

Through the body scan exercise, you are trying to notice sensations in the body and disconnect these sensations from your emotional and mental reactions to them. This provides a very important lesson, which is that you are constantly receiving messages of both wisdom and fearful propaganda from the body. These come from memories the body has stored and responses to events which your nervous system has accumulated. The body has an autobiography of its own which is largely unknown by the conscious mind.

Energy and information flow in the body: Polyvagal theory and trauma

Certain parts of the body store memories, experiences and reactions to experiences, especially trauma. In addition, the autonomic nervous system is primed for threat in response to past or current situations. The following examples illustrate this point:

1   If you were bitten by a dog as a child, it does not matter how much your mind is reassured that the dog you see approaching is gentle, your nervous system is still likely to show signs of stress and fear as it approaches.
2   If you were humiliated by a teacher in a maths class, the mere mention of maths may create sensations of shame and a desire for flight in your body.
3   If a humiliation came from conscious or unconscious racism or prejudice based on, for example, your difference to another person, your autonomic nervous system will be primed for future occurrences.
4   For some students, the smell of freshly mown grass can trigger anxiety because it signals the start of the exam period. This may seem surprising because for many other people the smell of freshly mown grass is a sign of Spring.

Very often when the nervous system has experienced stress in the past, it will have an instant reaction, sending signals of alarm to the amygdala (the alarm system in the brain) to generate stress hormones in the body milliseconds before the mind has been able to assess the situation. Once the stress response has begun, it is more difficult to keep the logical part of the mind functioning, so our thoughts can turn towards negative threat-driven thinking or it can freeze. How we react depends on the severity of the nervous reaction to events that occur all the time.

Recently, Porges (2011) identified the vagus nerve as the most powerful control centre of the nervous system. This is the largest system of nerves in the body. It flows from the brain stem all the way through the muscles and central organs of the body, regulating the body's basic functions. This nerve's primary function is to seek safety, homecoming and homeostasis in the body. In this pursuit it detects any signs of what it interprets as threat. This nerve does not communicate through thoughts but by the feelings and sensations in the body. It is from these vibes that safety or threat is communicated. It sends messages through sensations in the body, such as a gut feeling, a pounding heart, a sense of threat that the body experiences as stress. It also sends messages of safety or familiarity that the body can relax with.

Once the vagus nerve has identified what it perceives as a threat, it sends signals to the rest of the body to start producing the chemicals and bodily preparations of the stress response. It communicates this message to the heart and lungs. Menakem (2021) calls it the 'soul nerve', as it expresses much of what it means to be human and communicates not just within the body but to other bodies. For example, you can walk into a room and sense others' tension, atmosphere or lightness. This sense may intensify if you are obviously different from the majority of people in a group.

"When your body has an emotional response, such as when your stomach clenches, your voice catches, the pulse races, your breathing quickens, your body braces for impact, or you have a sense that danger is lurking, that's your soul nerve at work." (Menakem, 2021: 140)

Menakem illustrates how trauma may be held in the body of a person of colour because of the history and context of being in an environment of racial inequality. This topic has been widely discussed in student mindfulness groups recently because of raised consciousness due to the high-profile murder of George Floyd in 2020 – another triggering event as previously described – and the increasing strength of the Black Lives Matter (BLM) movement. Black students and students of colour can experience a sense of threat if they move from a place of hyper-diversity such as London to a less diverse regional campus. A recent report by the Equalities and Human Rights Commission found that 24 per cent of students from Black and Ethnic Minority backgrounds had experienced racial harassment and micro-aggressions on campus (EHRC, 2019). This can cause tension which can be unconscious because the body and nervous system are picking up a sense of threat and fear and the need to be hyper-vigilant at all times. At the same time, because racism has an impact on all of us, White students can experience tension which can be unconscious, based on an awareness of their privilege and the impact of inequality. Resources on the experience of being Black and of colour, white privilege, white fragility and how to be a good ally are included at the end of the chapter.

For many people, stress in the body can be triggered by a sense of threat, which may be heightened at night or when walking in the dark alone. This sense of danger is also communicated through the body and can cause sensations of fear and panic. There has been heightened concern on campuses in UK universities around personal safety since the tragic death of Sarah Everard in the UK in March 2021, and the alarming rise in 'spiking'. Spiking is defined by Rape Crisis (2021) as

"when somebody puts alcohol or drugs into another person's drink or their body without their knowledge and/or consent."

The practice of mindfulness can help mitigate at least some stress by recognising what is happening. Siegel (2012) describes this as extending our 'window of tolerance' to stay with things which have in the past dysregulated us and, instead of avoiding difficulty, going towards it in our minds so that we can have a better understanding of our anxieties.

Rightly or wrongly, whether arising from past or present, your brain stem reacts. Conversely, when your body feels relaxed, open and settled, your vagus nerve is functioning well. Therefore, one of the most positive things of being able to identify signals from the body, without getting pulled into reactive states from the mind and emotions, is that it can allow us to regulate when we feel anxious. This enables the mind and body to come back to a state of balance so that when the body is safe enough to connect with the wiser, thinking mind, there is regulation from impulsive reaction.

> "… you will discover, with some attention and patience, you can learn to work with your soul nerve. With practice, you can begin to consciously and deliberately relax your muscles, settle your body, and soothe yourself during difficult or high-stress situations. This will help you avoid reflexively sliding into a fight, flee or freeze response in situations where such response is unnecessary." (Menakem, 2017: 140)

Mindfulness has been identified as one of those practices that can help us gain such control. Regulation means recovering more quickly from upsets and having more freedom from impulsive reactions. It can help us to observe our emotions but not be driven by them. If we think back to Olu's story through the lens of science and the shifts and changes in her body and thoughts, it might look a bit like this. When she doesn't get a text response, her body and mind go into a state of dysregulation, most likely informed by a history of feeling rejected and not being good enough.

The need to feel a sense of belonging and connection is very important for all of us and it is especially important for students. Many students move away from home to go to university. This may involve moving from one part of the country to another, perhaps from a small town to a large city, or it may mean moving from one country to another. This can be an exciting and stimulating experience, although it is also stressful and there is a process of transition, which can, at times, be very difficult as you let go of your past friends and identity and make new friends. In our own experience of running mindfulness groups on campus, we have observed that such groups can provide much-needed support and a sense of community to students. A supportive mindfulness group gives students a sense of connection which acts as a counterbalance to the anonymity of large lecture spaces, online services and high student numbers.

As we mentioned in the introduction; Stephen Covey says "We see the world, not as it is, but as we are—or, as we are conditioned to see it." In any group, different people will respond differently to the same event. In other words, the same situation can be interpreted in many different ways by individuals, and in different ways by the same person according to their mood. Over the years writers and philosophers have explained this phenomenon in different ways. For example, the Greek philosopher, Epictetus, said, 'It is not the things that happen to us that are upsetting, but the view we take of these things.' The more we interpret things in a negative way, the higher the levels of stress hormones such as cortisol are raised, which has a negative impact of not being able to concentrate and think. This is not to say that discrimination based on racism, sexism or homophobia is not a reality, but mindfulness is a way which helps us to respond wisely rather than in a way that is harmful to ourselves.

Pleasant events

A final focus for this chapter is on *pleasant events*. We can explore and notice pleasant events and become aware of the effect they have on our body, thoughts, emotions and impulse to act. Focusing on pleasant events as they happen can create positive chemical shifts in the body, such as collecting serotonin; our mood generator, and dopamine; our reward centre. The more we tune in to beautiful things, the more open we become to perceiving beautiful things in the everyday. This has a very positive effect on our mood, body and immunology.

Student perspective 2

"*My journey in mindfulness has enabled me to connect with my spiritual values and has made me become aware of the existence of a greater positive energy within myself. My personal experience of mindfulness has supported me to deal with the grief that arose from a traumatic bereavement. I entered the 5 week mindfulness course as a young student in great denial, confusion and silent pain. Having engaged and participated in various meditation sessions, I resonated the most with the body scan exercise, as this helped me to become aware of the changes to my body regarding the physical and emotional sensations that arose from my thoughts. Alongside the body scan, engaging in weekly learning involving mindful movement and reflection allowed me to perceive my thoughts without judgement and greater acceptance. Each session, combined with my engagement in weekly homework practices, enabled me to embrace every emotion and thought I experienced without avoidance. Up until now, the body scan has been the most impactful meditative exercise for me, and I continue to engage with this practice when I begin to experience a sense of discomfort within myself. I am forever grateful for having been introduced to the practice of mindfulness and I continue to encourage other individuals who have experienced bereavement at schools, university and colleagues at work to begin their own journey of mindfulness.*" (Halpana Shritharan, Psychology student)

Lesson Plan: Session 2
Session aim: Understand body and mind connections and question assumptions

Objectives:
1. Connect with the body
2. Identify physical responses to stress
3. Identify and question assumptions to everyday events
4. Understand the importance of noticing pleasant events

Activities:	Time:
1. Introduce the body scan and guide the meditation	15 minutes
2. Enquiry	15 minutes
3. Group share experiences from last week of doing something mindfully everyday	15 minutes
4. Explain and discuss how the body reacts to stress	10 minutes
5. Walking down the road exercise	15 minutes
6. Introduce pleasant events calendar	10 minutes
7. Short Breathing Space Meditation and close	10 minutes

Notes:
1. The body scan is a simple exercise which is usually done lying down, but can be done in any comfortable posture. We do this exercise for two main reasons. First, to build the muscles of attention, which helps us to focus and recognise thoughts when they arise and take us away from our focus. Second, to tune in to the tiny sensations in the body that we might not otherwise notice. The aim is to notice them with curiosity and kindness, not judgement or worry.
2. For the enquiry, ask questions such as:
    - *What did you notice? Where did you feel it? What did you do after that? Did anyone else have that experience?*
    - *Did anybody have a sensation of restlessness or boredom? Did you notice what that is like and where it turns up in the body? Did you notice the thoughts attached to it?*
    - *What happens if we listen to it with compassion and not resist it but wait for it to shift?*
    - *Do any of you have this experience when studying? What do you do when that happens? How do you refocus? Any good or bad suggestions?*
3. Each person's experiences of mindful activities needs to be validated, even if some members of the group weren't able to find time to do the homework.
4. Students think about their physical reaction to a stressful event such as an exam, a presentation or a deadline. Brainstorm how this feels in the body, e.g. shaking, heart beating faster, sweaty hands.
5. Tell students the following story: *You are walking down the road and you see a friend walking on the other side of the road towards you. You wave effusively at them. They blank you and walk past.* Write four columns and ask students to tell you what their first response was and then go through the different responses and how they arise in the different columns. From this exercise we learn that the same event can be interpreted in many different ways. Therefore, we have an experience on three different levels: the thing or situation itself, the way we interpret or perceive it, and the way we develop thoughts and interpret it, which we believe is the truth when it may well be a distortion of our experiences.

6. Mindfulness teaches us to take notice of the small pleasant events which happen every day, such as the sound of birds, the smell of flowers or the taste of your favourite food. This week's homework is for students to start to notice and record these pleasant events.
7. End the session with a short guided Breathing Space Meditation (see Chapter 1 for script, which can be adapted for longer or shorter meditations depending on the time you have). This is the most flexible of meditations, which students can use whenever they feel they want to.

Homework:
1. Practise the body scan 5–6 times in the week.
2. Notice and record pleasant events in a pleasant events calendar.
3. Use the Breathing Space Meditation as often as you need to during the week.

Example: Walking down the road

What happened?	What sensations occur in your body?	What emotions do you feel?	What thoughts do you have?
My friend blanked me	Blow to the tummy	Fear/shame	What have I done?

Pleasant events calendar

It is important to record the events and to answer all columns of how you feel and think about the event when you bring it to mind and how it might affect your behaviour or impulse to act.

Day	What happened?	What sensations occurred in your body?	What thoughts did you have?
Monday			
Tuesday			
Wednesday			
Thursday			
Friday			
Saturday			
Sunday			

Resources

Quick and easy reads

Kivel, P. (2006) Guidelines for Being Strong White Allies. Adapted from *Uprooting Racism: How White People Can Work for Social Justice*. https://drive.google.com/file/d/1VHw4nGfDogf7-SaftsCzxosQ19lTB4uz/view [accessed 8 May 2021].

Laws, C. (2020) White people, here's how we can be better allies and anti-racist, *Glamour Magazine*. https://www.glamourmagazine.co.uk/article/how-to-be-a-white-ally [accessed 8 May 2021].

Lopez, G. (2016) Why you should stop saying 'all lives matter' explained in 9 different ways, *Vox*. https://www.vox.com/2016/7/11/12136140/black-all-lives-matter [accessed 8 May 2021].

McIntosh, P. (1989) White Privilege: Unpacking the Invisible Knapsack. Seeking Educational Equality and Diversity. https://nationalseedproject.org/Key-SEED-Texts/white-privilege-unpacking-the-invisible-knapsack [accessed 8 May 2021].

Rajan-Rankin, S. (2020) Is Covid-19 an 'equal opportunity disease'?, *Social Work 2020–21 under Covid-19 Magazine*. https://sw2020covid19.group.shef.ac.uk/2020/04/24/is-covid-19-an-equal-opportunity-disease/ [accessed 8 May 2021].

Shepherd, M. (2020) Racial microaggressions in science, *Forbes*, 18 February. https://www.forbes.com/sites/marshallshepherd/2020/02/18/racial-microaggressions-in-science/?sh=5aa16c7b4900 [accessed 8 May 2021].

Longer reads

DiAngelo, R. (2019) *White Fragility: Why It's So Hard for White People to Talk about Racism*. London: Penguin.

Eddo-Lodge, R. (2017) *Why I'm No Longer Talking to White People about Race*. London: Bloomsbury.

Hirsch, A. (2018) *Brit(ish): On Race, Identity and Belonging*. London: Vintage.

Kendi, I.X. (2019) *How to Be an Antiracist*. London: The Bodley Head.

Oluo, I. (2018) *So You Want to Talk About Race*. Ashland, OR: Blackstone Audio.

Rutherford, A. (2020) *How to Argue with a Racist: History, Science, Race and Reality*. London: Weidenfeld & Nicolson.

Shukla, N. (2016) *The Good Immigrant*. London: Unbound.

References

Equalities and Human Rights Commission (EHRC) (2019) *Tackling Racial Harassment: Universities Challenged*. https://www.equalityhumanrights.com/sites/default/files/tackling-racial-harassment-universities-challenged.pdf [accessed 22 March 2021].

Gilbert, P. (2013) *The Compassionate Mind*, 3rd edition. London: Constable & Robinson.

Goleman, D. and Davidson, R. (2017) *Altered Traits: Science Reveals How Meditation Changes Your Mind, Brain and Body*. New York: Avery Publishing.

Menakem, R. (2021) *My Grandmother's Hands: Racialised Trauma and the Pathway to Mending Our Hearts and Bodies*. London: Penguin.

Porges, S.W. (2011) *The Polyvagal Theory: Neurophysiological Foundations of Emotions, Attachment, Communication, and Self-regulation*. New York: W.W. Norton.

Rape Crisis (2021) *Types of Sexual Violence.* https://rapecrisis.org.uk/get-informed/types-of-sexual-violence/what-is-spiking/ [last accessed 20 December 2021].

Saron, C. (2013) Training the mind: The Samantha Project, in A. Frazer (ed.) *The Healing Power of Meditation.* Boston, MA: Shambhala.

Siegel, D. (2012) *A Pocket Guide to Interpersonal Neurobiology: An Integrative Handbook of the Mind.* New York: W.W. Norton.

3 Staying present

Sam's story

Sam is a 37-year-old mature student approaching the last hurdle before completing his PhD. This is a dream he has coveted for the past seven years, postponing it whilst he tried to make a living for his young family. Sam arrived at a mindfulness session as an absolute last resort. He felt terrible, exhausted all the time but he was having trouble sleeping, with low-lying anxiety constantly present. He felt unable to focus and unmotivated, and upset with himself because he was being so bad tempered with his young family.

When he had embarked on the PhD, Sam had felt passionately about the subject he was studying and hoped it would contribute positively to his field of work and society. However, over the past few years he had become more worn down. He was struggling financially, and as his family was growing they were in need of more space. He was finding it extremely hard to complete his studies, and his supervisor was pushing him to write papers to deliver at conferences, which he knew he needed to do if he was to pursue an academic career. However, he had lost his drive to do anything with his career or his home life, and he was becoming increasingly depressed. His family wanted more of his time and were keen for him to complete his thesis, so he was feeling pressure, torn between his studies and his family. He was also struggling with his health. He was not looking after himself or his diet, and he was having terrible headaches and stomach problems.

Sam was feeling so unmotivated that he had fallen into some habits that were increasing his anxiety and sense of being overwhelmed. As often happens when we get very busy, Sam had given up the things that nourished him. Sam was no longer able to enjoy playing with his children. He felt too tired to get out into the fresh air and exercise, so he was isolating in his room. He sat for hours at his computer but he was not able to focus, so he got into the habit of flicking through links on the internet, without a clear focus, his mind wandering and taking him down some very destructive pathways.

These are all warning signs for anxiety and depression. Sam was at the early stages of this, so he was able to reach out for help. For others, if depression has become entrenched, they will need to consult a medical professional for help and they will need added support to manage symptoms. At these times, anything which involves self-help such as mindfulness can be counterproductive as it can reinforce a sense of failure if a person cannot find the motivation for even the smallest practices. In Sam's case, mindfulness was a useful tool for gently starting to manage his symptoms and gain some sense of control in life. For Sam, understanding what was happening to him in his body, mind, biochemistry and emotions was a start to help him realise he could make some small positive changes in his life.

Explanation: Depression and anxiety – signs and symptoms

Everyone is unique and you may experience some or none of the symptoms detailed below in relation to anxiety and depression. Your GP can complete an assessment and offer you further advice and guidance.

Common signs and symptoms of depression include finding it hard to motivate yourself to do everyday tasks like getting out of bed, getting washed and dressed, cooking, eating and, of course, studying. People experiencing depression may also find it difficult to concentrate, feel numb, sleep for long periods but not feel refreshed, or disconnect from friends and family. The mental health charity MIND provides more information and guidance on what to look out for. A link to their organisation can be found at the end of this chapter.

Research by Hari (2018) identifies seven areas of lost connection that are repeatedly identified in people with anxiety and depression and who are lonely. These are:

1 Disconnection from your inner world
2 Disconnection from other people
3 Disconnection from meaningful values
4 Disconnection from sympathetic joy and addiction to the self
5 Disconnection from the natural world
6 Disconnection from community and helping others
7 Disconnection from a secure future acknowledging and overcoming childhood trauma.

Hari (2021) describes his own experience of depression and anxiety and cites the ever-growing numbers of people experiencing mental health problems. He says that although we know drugs can help, depression and anxiety are much less about chemical imbalance and much more to do with the way we live. Hari recognises that human beings need to get together for a common purpose with shared goals and vision for the future. He advocates establishing community groups for people experiencing anxiety and depression to create something together such as a garden. In this way, people can discover a sense of community and establish goals which give meaning and purpose to their lives. They can start to recreate 'a tribe', the most important aspect of which is conveying a sense of belonging, which can lead to remarkable improvements in people's wellbeing. Our ancestors had been aware of this antidote to present-day mental health issues since the beginning of time.

As we have learnt already, much of our nervous system dates back to earlier times when humans' survival depended on tuning into and defending against imminent threat of being eaten or maimed by larger animals. We know that the polyvagal nerve is constantly seeking safety and belonging, so this, coupled with adverse circumstances in our past, can keep us permanently on the lookout for threat and hyper-vigilant to anything we interpret is a risk to our sense of security and belonging. Therefore, we have an automatic bias towards seeing threats. This increases when we feel stressed and overwhelmed; we begin to tune into anything risky. We then turn to what we believe to be the trusty territory of the brain to help us think our way through this. However, it is the default position of anxiety to overthink, especially for people whose minds are treasured and applauded such as students in higher education. We now know that thinking and reviewing over and over again can contribute to compulsive overthinking and rumination, thus digging a deep hole-of-helplessness.

Mouse and the maze

An interesting piece of research carried out by Friedman and Forster (2001, cited by Williams and Penman, 2011) reports on a psychology experiment undertaken by a class of students. The students were divided into two groups. Both groups were told that they had to help a mouse find its way out of a maze. Group 1 was incentivised by the promise of a piece of cheese for the mouse when it completed its journey. Group 2 was warned that the mouse must escape the maze quickly because there was an owl ready to pounce on it. The task was easy and both groups of students succeeded in getting the mouse out of the maze. However, the after effects of the experiment were profound. At the end of the experiment, the students undertook a series of unrelated creative tasks. Students in group 2 who were fearful for the mouse because of the threat of the owl were found to be 50 per cent less creative and risk-averse. In contrast, students in group 1, who had been incentivised by the thought of the mouse being rewarded with cheese, were playful, experimental and productive.

This experiment confirms what we know about work-related stress. Many people who find themselves in a cycle of stress because of work try to work their way out of it. However, the more they push themselves, the worse they feel. Through mindfulness practice you can learn to recognise the triggers which activate your stress response. Sometimes the best course of action is to stop working and instead allow yourself time to nourish and nurture yourself. It is important to remember that we need to keep our reward centres open by recognising the beauty in our world. These acts of self-nourishment and self-nurture can be personal to you, but through our work with many students over the years recurrent themes have arisen, such as spending time in nature, exercising, dancing, listening to or playing music, spending time with friends and family, cooking or being creative. These can be regarded as soothing activities, which we know are really important to regulate and balance your body and mind.

It is important to try to ensure that each day contains at least one nurturing or soothing activity. This becomes even more important when you are feeling stressed or anxious, such as when the deadline for an assessment is fast approaching. Use the form below to write a list of the things that you do which nurture, soothe and restore you.

Nurturing/soothing/restorative activities

#

#

#

#

#

Research into work-related stress has found that the default human reaction to prolonged adverse circumstances is a feeling of helplessness and panic (Seligman, 2016). The only way we can influence this sense of helplessness is to gain some sense of control and autonomy over our condition and find pathways to lead us to the more logical and productive function. This can be found in the prefrontal cortex of the brain. Accessing this wider, less fear-driven part of the brain can help us to truly assess what is going on and how to quieten the threat system in the body. Therefore, gaining some control over work/life balance often means letting go of the tight control that you may have constructed to try to 'push through' work stress. Although it feels counterintuitive, it is only by letting go and allowing others to take control of aspects of life that you can then start to regain a sense of control and agency over your priorities. This is important for students because it enables them to reach out to friends, family and tutors for support. Pressure points such as revising for exams, doing a dissertation or writing up a large project are often stressful times for students.

Procrastination/time management

One common reaction to work-related stress is procrastination. Students have always suffered from procrastination, but in the twenty-first century this is amplified by easy access to the internet and social media. Many thousands of hours are lost every year by students aimlessly clicking on links that have little or no relevance to the research they are supposed to be doing. Likewise, many students procrastinate by endlessly checking social media updates. Search engines and social media platforms are programmed to identify our hopes, fears and preoccupations. Knowing us so well, they feed our addictions and neuroses by targeted messages and adverts. Therefore, we need to know ourselves before algorithms know us better and start dictating who we are and how we think (Harari, 2018).

Sam limited his use of the internet so he was not inadvertently feeding his anxieties and in doing so he gained some small mastery over his tendency to lose hours procrastinating in this way. Through mindfulness practice he was able to watch the thoughts in his head which increased his anxiety and then learn how to let them go. This allowed him to make a choice about what to do next. One of the important things to remember about the kind of depression that Sam was moving into is that we cannot wait to become motivated to act. This means that you need to take action first and be prepared to wait for motivation to occur later. There are some simple steps which you can take to limit procrastination and dependence on the internet and social media.

1 Action precedes motivation: a tiny action of mastery or control can begin to give you a sense of control. For example, take regular breaks from the internet or social media, change a habit; instead of trawling the internet aimlessly, take a walk at lunchtime. These small changes can give you a sense of reward and an accompanying small dose of *dopamine* to feed your motivation.

2 Connect and be as present as you can for even the smallest of moments with friends, family and strangers. This produces the feel-good social bonding chemical *oxytocin*.

3 Open your reward centre to appreciate little things in life. Notice the effect of everyday pleasant events; such as watching a beautiful sunset, hearing children's laughter, enjoying good food and taking gentle exercise. This will be explored more as we look at our experiences of the pleasant events which produce the mood-enhancing chemical *serotonin*.

4 It has been said that sitting is the present generation's smoking in terms of the damage it does to the body, the immune system, cognition and overall mental wellbeing (Ilard, 2013). Therefore, for optimum wellbeing we need to move our bodies even in the smallest ways as this can promote the motivation to enhance the *endorphins*. The smallest movements can produce great effects in releasing muscles and generating a sense of happiness and boosting our immune systems. We will explore this more when looking at this week's practice of mindful movement below.

Producing the happiness quartet of chemicals – dopamine, oxytocin, serotonin and endorphins (DOSE) – is our greatest defence against the anxiety and depression chemicals of adrenaline and cortisol. These negative chemicals were wiring Sam's mind and body and depriving it of energy, focus and hope. For all of us, ensuring we get a daily DOSE is an effective defence against stress and anxiety. These small changes surprisingly gave Sam more productive time as his mood began to lift. He felt more energetic and found it easier to laugh and have small moments of pleasure. Through mindfulness practice Sam was able to understand his stress response and be curious about how the habits he developed increased his stress and anxiety. He began to see how he could manage stress and anxiety in a different and more productive way.

Slowly, Sam began to recognise how important it is to keep a focus on the small, pleasant things which make life feel worthwhile. Over time Sam noticed how his attitude towards spending time with his children could be a part of his mindfulness practice. He realised that spending time being present, walking and talking with his children nourished him. Formal mindfulness practice was difficult for Sam in terms of time and space, so it was important for him to find ways to fit it in. Therefore, he developed short practices of mindfulness that included focusing on the breath while sitting on the train to and from the university, short walking meditations between writing periods in the library, and mindful washing-up and cleaning at home. This practice enabled Sam to regain his sense of meaning and purpose, and he found that instead of dreading and resenting his PhD, he was able to reconnect with it and enjoy the tasks of researching and writing.

In the first two chapters of this book, we looked at how we can 'drop into' the present using the breath and body. We can regulate ourselves with the help of the breath and we can begin to listen to the body and the messages of the nervous system with some discernment rather than ignoring it or powerlessly being driven by our fear responses or impulses. We have learnt about the uses and deficits of assumptions and automatic-pilot reactions. We have been slowly learning that not only are thoughts not facts, but that with regular practice we can begin to manage our thoughts and choose when to go with them. If this is done in a context of loving, kind, patient, non-judgement towards ourselves, it can help us to take more care of ourselves, think more clearly and calm the impulses of our nervous system.

Practice: Mindful movement

The meditation for this chapter is mindful movement. It takes the principles of the body scan and uses the same kind and curious attention to our bodies in motion. This enables us to begin to understand the connection between mind and body. Some people, especially those used to working mainly in their heads, have lost all contact with the needs of their bodies. Mindful movement can be very slight and gentle movements that can ripple through the body. The movements allow us to develop an awareness of how stress affects different parts of the body, such as the head, the neck or the shoulders. They can be introduced standing up or sitting down.

The introduction is to offer an opportunity to really ground and then practise a cooperative relationship with your body. This is not about moving towards an end product or goal but about really noticing the messages and tiny micro-movements in the body coming from outside and inside. For some students, this can be a relief as it is something clear to focus on. For others, especially those who have lived mainly in their heads, this can be difficult because it may trigger negative memories associated with any kind of physical exercise. Mindful movement can be particularly difficult for students with some neural diversity or physical disabilities or students whose bodies have been ridiculed or abused. Therefore, it is best to start with non-exposing gentle movements until you get to know the students' responses.

In mindful movement it is not the movement itself which is important, but the noticing and cultivating kindness towards tuning into the body. This will help to make sure you are gently going towards your edge, not pushing your edge in a bid to fit in, which can result in overstretching the body, nor resisting the stretch through fear and habit thus keeping the body locked. This edge-point and the accompanying recognition of choice-points can help us gain control and recognise how our bodies are not static things but instead are constantly interacting and being influenced by the people, information, environment and circumstances around us. What's more, we are influenced by the inner shifts that can occur beyond our consciousness in reaction to things around us.

> "Although our bodies are complete, they are also constantly changing. Our bodies are literally immersed in a larger whole, namely the environment, the planet, the universe." (Kabat-Zinn, 2013: 163)

This quote from Kabat-Zinn indicates that when we tune into the messages in the body and learn how to relieve physical tightness, it has a ripple effect which moves through our nervous system and shifts the chemicals in our body. This allows us to gain control of our bodies and feel connected to our physical selves. Thus, we begin to make the connection between our bodies and our mood, recognising that regular exercise and exposure to the outside can really boost our mood state by releasing endorphins. Through mindfulness practice at any time, we can tune into the body and gently lift the shoulders or neck, releasing energy. The more mindful we become and the more compassionate we are to ourselves, the more compassionate we will become towards those around us, all other sentient beings and the planet itself.

Meditation: Mindful Movement (followed by a breathing space)

Settle into a comfortable seated position, cross-legged on the floor or straight-backed on a chair, wherever is most comfortable for you. Let your arms rest on your lap, or by your sides. Close your eyes or lower your gaze and turn your attention inwards. This is like a pause, or a signal to yourself that this is your time to connect with yourself. Try to notice how you feel right now, without judgement, and take a deep breath in and then slowly release out. Do this a couple of times.

Now, focus on your shoulders. Lift your right shoulder up towards your right ear and then slowly lower it back down remembering to breathe gently with the movement. Now do the same on the left side. Pause and check how you are experiencing these movements. Try to bring your awareness to the micro-movements that are happening within your body as you raise and lower your shoulders. Repeat this movement four or five times. As you raise your shoulders take an intentional breath in, and as you lower them breathe gently out and return to your original position.

Now, focus on one shoulder and slowly rotate your shoulder all the way around in one direction and then all the way around in the opposite direction, noticing as you do this how your shoulder and neck feel. Then turn your attention to the other shoulder and again slowly rotate your shoulder in one direction all the way around and then in the opposite direction all the way around, pausing in between to notice how this feels.

Now, gently rotate both shoulders together all the way around in one direction and then all the way around in the opposite direction. When you are doing this, focus your attention on how this movement feels.

Now, raise one arm out and up above your head and turn your head to look towards your raised hand above you. Open your eyes and look at your hand and stretch again as if you are reaching to pick a piece of fruit from a branch of a tree which is just beyond your reach. As you stretch up, notice how your body feels and try to stretch your fingers just a little further, pausing to feel this micro-movement. Slowly release the stretch and repeat on the other side of your body. (You may find this movement easier on one side of your body than the other, so don't push yourself if it begins to hurt.)

Now, take your arms down and hold them out at about hip height and move your arms together from left to right moving your whole torso with your arms in a slow, twisting movement four or five times. As you twist, try to locate the feelings in your torso as it moves from one side to the other.

Finally, clasp your hands together behind your neck, at the base of your head. Breathe in deeply and let go of your breath slowly. Repeat this three or four times. Then relax your arms, bringing them back down to rest in your lap or by your sides. Give your body a final breath in and out, taking time to notice any feelings or emotions which are present. When you are ready, gently open your eyes and return your attention to the room.

As we have already seen in Chapters 1 and 2, the Breathing Space Meditation is a quick portable practice that you can use to ground yourself throughout the day. It is adaptable depending on the time you have. The 3 minute practice that appears below involves stopping and pausing, then dropping your attention into the body and noticing any tension or ease there. This simply creates a small pause. The breathing space can be used as a choice-point to interrupt a habit, automatic pilot or the stress response.

Meditation: Breathing Space

1 Drop your attention into the body and notice any tension or ease there.
2 Turn your attention to your thoughts and general mood and take five mindfulness breaths.
3 As best you can, keep your full attention on your breath and then expand your awareness again to the body, mind and emotions.
4 Broaden your awareness to include your five senses: sight, touch, sound, taste and smell.
5 When you are ready, gently turn your attention outwards again.

Reflection: Mind and body connection

After the Mindful Movement Meditation, students usually report feeling more open in their movements and they have a greater sense of wellbeing and lightness. This is a wonderful cocktail for producing your own serotonin, the mood-enhancing brain chemical. We notice how little the movements are and that when we are experiencing moments of happiness and peace, our movements are often opening. Research into the physiology of thoughts reveals how our mood can be affected by the shape and range of our movements. Moreover, not only are we affected emotionally by certain movements, but also our moods can shift just by watching some movements, for example in dance performances or the universal movement of raising your arms in victory (Christensen and Gomila, 2018). Indeed, it is difficult to feel low with your arms stretched above your head.

This observation was affirmed by Cuddy's research (2015). She explored the connection between certain body poses and the chemical effects they can have on the body and how this affects our performances. For example, she found that downward slouching poses cause negative cortisol, whereas stretching-upwards movements produce mood-enhancing serotonin. If you practise standing in the power pose for a few moments, you can feel the effects on your own body. This is particularly useful for students to do just before sitting an exam or delivering a presentation. Experiencing or remembering pleasant events can create a similar sense of wellbeing in the body and produce a smile that sends a message of safety and belonging akin to secure attachment to our nervous systems.

Therefore, it is important to stop and really absorb even the smallest moments of pleasure or gratitude because they can really enhance your sense of wellbeing emotionally, mentally and physically. Noticing these moments develops your receptors and opens your reward centres so you notice and retain more deeply these treasured moments. It really is true that the more you do so, the more you notice. So, it is useful to tune into your receptors and develop a reservoir of pleasant events to call upon when you need them.

Another valuable lesson of mindfulness which we introduced in Chapter 2 is that thoughts are not facts. The poem below picks up on this theme. It has been adapted to a study context from Portia Nelson's poem *Autobiography in five short chapters*. The message of this poem is that you can change the way you view things, and you can choose how to react. It also reminds us of the destructive power of the stress response, which can sabotage our minds and leave us feeling unable to think straight.

Lesson Plan: Session 3
Session aim: To help students develop personal strategies to positive thinking
Objectives: 1. Understand that noticing the small wonders in everyday life helps combat low mood 2. Identify how stress is triggered and its physical impact

Activities:	Time:
1. Mindful Movement Meditation going into mindful breath	20 minutes
2. Enquiry	15 minutes
3. Feedback from the pleasant events diary. Move from individual responses into the experiences of the whole group. Introduce unpleasant events	15 minutes
4. Review body scan experiences	10 minutes
5. Explain the mouse in the maze experiment and what it teaches us	10 minutes
6. The power of body language and set homework	15 minutes

Notes:

1. Guide students in a Mindful Movement Meditation. In this exercise it is important to only do what is comfortable and find your 'edge' between trying to follow the instructions and knowing when to stop. Tell students to try to listen to the needs/edges of their body, not the dictator in their mind or the need to get it right. When this ends, go straight into a very short Breathing Space Meditation.
2. Ask students to reflect on the mindful movement and notice feelings which arose. It is important to note that some people find mindful movement easier than still mindfulness; for others it is more difficult. In time you can incorporate mindful movement when you are walking or doing your own form of exercise. This can be mindful if the mind and body are yoked and not lost in thoughts; if you are focused on the process itself rather than an end goal and if you can bring kindness and patience to the process.
3. Tell students that identifying regular pleasant events is a strategy to help combat low mood because it helps us to recognise the small wonders in everyday life. Recognising this is a medication-free way of collecting serotonin, the feel-good chemical.
4. Ask students the following questions without judgement, just curiosity:
   - *Did the body scan affect your mood or wellbeing this week?*
   - *Have you noticed any change in your mindful routine activity?*
5. Explain and discuss the experiment and what can be learned from it. Fear does not produce good results; creative thinking and problem-solving can be incentivised with rewards.
6. Share with the group the Power Pose, 'Your body language may shape who you are' Ted Talk (Cuddy, 2012) and explain the home practice tasks for this week.

Homework:

1. Practise mindful movement.
2. Alternate daily with body scan.
3. Repeat pleasant events diary and start recording unpleasant events.
4. Practise breathing space as many times a day as you feel you need to.

This session focuses on our own triggers which set off the stress response and on how we can best attend to them. It looks at what happens in the brain when we feel stressed. This helps us to recognise the patterns of response which sustain us and the automatic pilot patterns of response which exacerbate stress.

Mindful Movement Meditation focuses on how mindful practice can be taken into movement. If this feels difficult or uncomfortable, it is fine to remain sitting or even just to imagine that you are moving. The important thing is to try to focus on the movement. Watch out for any thoughts that try to take your focus away, especially those which tell you that you are doing it wrong, you are not doing it the same as others, or which make you feel waves of self-consciousness. Try to practise turning towards these thoughts or feelings with curiosity, not judgement. Try to not react to them, but instead, really notice how these thoughts affect your mood and body. Consider what happens if you do not resist or build these thoughts but just accept that they are there and gently let them pass by.

Some people find mindful movement easier than still mindfulness; for others it is more difficult. In time you can incorporate mindful movement when you are walking or doing your own form of exercise. This can be mindful if the mind and body are connected and not lost in thoughts; if you are focused on the process itself rather than an end goal and if you can bring kindness and patience to the process.

Cultivating moments of happiness in a pleasant events diary and really acknowledging a sense of gratitude has been shown to give a great boost to our emotional, social, physical and mental wellbeing. Brown (2020) found that most people report that when they experience a pleasant event their thoughts are very few and, if left alone, the mind is still and appreciative for a while. These moments can refresh and renew us, giving us a small dose of serotonin to help buffer us against the stresses of the day. However, it is hard for some people to just stay with this feeling. This is because they are so tuned into the possibility of what can go wrong: they find it hard to stay with the present. They start looking for evidence of the way things could go wrong and start hypothesising or analysing possible problems. They think that this will enable them to control the world or prepare themselves better by thinking of worst-case scenarios. This is like punishing yourself to be more motivated; it doesn't work. It simply replaces the joyous potential of serotonin with caustic cortisol and denies you the pleasure of that moment.

Unpleasant events

Using the same format used for pleasant events, add an awareness of unpleasant events. Continue to log the pleasant events as this has such a rich effect, but add a couple of experiences of noticing the impact on your body, mind and mood of even the slightest difficult or unpleasant event. During an unpleasant event the body tends to contract: the mind focuses on negative thoughts and emotions, and your mood plummets. This helps us understand when a difficulty becomes stress and prompts the stress response and the release of adrenalin. This is useful when running for our lives, but destructive in our desk-bound modern life. Try to make sure that the event you choose is a small irritation rather than a big stress.

Give students an example of a small unpleasant event, such as being splashed with rainwater by a passing vehicle, or running out of milk in the morning.

Discuss how unpleasant events may manifest in sensations, emotions and thoughts and our impulse to act and think. Suggest students keep an unpleasant events record and keep the pleasant events diary going at the same time to keep their reward centres open.

Resources: anxiety and depression

MIND information on anxiety: https://www.mind.org.uk/information-support/types-of-mental-health-problems/depression/symptoms/#Anxiety

MIND information on depression: https://www.mind.org.uk/information-support/types-of-mental-health-problems/depression/symptoms/#CommonSignsAndSymptomsOf-Depression

References

Brown, B. (2020) *The Gifts of Imperfection*. London: Penguin.

Christensen, J.F. and Gomila, A. (2018) *Arts and the Brain: Psychology and Physiology Beyond Pleasure*, Progress in Brain Research Volume 237. London: Academic Press.

Cuddy, A. (2012) *Your body language may shape who you are*. TED Talk. https://www.ted.com/talks/amy_cuddy_your_body_language_may_shape_who_you_are?language=en.

Cuddy, A. (2015) *Presence: Bringing Your Boldest Self to Your Biggest Challenges*. New York: Little, Brown Spark.

Friedman, R.S. and Forster, J. (2001) The effects of promotion and prevention cues on creativity, *Journal of Personality and Social Psychology*, 81 (6): 1001–1013.

Harari, Y.N. (2018) *The two most important skills for the rest of your life*. https://youtu.be/x6tMLAjPVyo [last accessed 8 May 2021].

Hari, J. (2018) *Lost Connections: Uncovering the Real Causes of Depression – and the Unexpected Solutions*. London: Bloomsbury.

Hari, J. (2021) *This could be why you're depressed or anxious*. TED Talk. https://www.ted.com/talks/johann_hari_this_could_be_why_you_re_depressed_or_anxious?language=en

Ilard, S. (2013) *Brain chemistry lifehacks: Steve Ilardi at TEDxKC*. TEDx Talks. https://www.youtube.com/watch?v=8bnniNxqB4w [last accessed 8 May 2021].

Kabat-Zinn, J. (2013) *Full Catastrophe Living: How to Cope with Stress, Pain and Illness Using Mindfulness Meditation*. London: Piatkus Books.

Seligman, M. (2016) Positive Psychology presentation. https://www.actionforhappiness.org/martin-seligman-event [last accessed 8 May 2021].

Williams, M. and Penman, D. (2011) *Mindfulness: A Practical Guide to Finding Peace in a Frantic World*. London: Piatkus Books.

4 Thoughts are not facts

Ali's story

On 26 May 2020, Ali was in her final year of a Social Science degree. Living in London, but studying in Kent, she was at home revising for her finals and looking for jobs for the next phase of her life. But she had woken that day to hundreds of items on her Instagram page and Twitter feed. Looking at them, she had seen some of the sickening footage of a White policeman holding down a Black man by his neck until, after 9 minutes and 29 seconds, life ebbed away from him. She couldn't watch it. It upset her too much. Then she saw images and videos of the protests which turned to riots on the streets of the city in America where it had happened. It was thousands of miles away, but it was also so close; close to the experiences of her friends, her family and members of her community. Boys from her school had been stopped and searched repeatedly by the police. A young man from her street, who had been an innocent bystander at a road traffic incident, had been tasered by a policeman for refusing to kneel down in front of him.

That day was so emotional and overwhelming. Ali felt horror, sadness, anger, disbelief, exhaustion, frustration, shock, powerlessness and rage. She knew that she could not accept what was going on. She couldn't absorb all of those feelings and carry on with her life unchanged. She absolutely could not come to a mindful acceptance of this situation. But even in the hurricane of emotions, she was able to remember that mindfulness doesn't teach you to ignore your feelings; it teaches you to pause and choose how to respond. This pause enabled Ali to locate an emotion at the core of the hurricane; a feeling of solidarity and purpose to do something; to channel her anger into action. She knew that she needed to use her emotional energy to stand up for her beliefs, but she wasn't sure that she had the strength to do so.

Whenever we are faced with difficulties that remind us of our vulnerabilities it is natural to try to push them away. Ali felt that she had done that many times when she had witnessed injustice. She had felt anger and sadness, but also a sense of powerlessness which had made her passive. She had tried to ignore the difficulties and get on with her life. She studied hard and got a place at university, burying herself in work and trying to improve her life. But in this situation, she could not turn away even though it scared her to think about the impact her action might have on her own life. It would distract her from her finals and her job hunt. It might change the way some of her White friends treated her. It might worry her parents and her family and bring them unwanted attention at work or in the neighbourhood. But she realised that this was too big to turn away from. She realised that she had to turn towards it. She knew that she could not carry on pretending that events like these had nothing to do with her and that if she didn't turn towards this difficulty, she would become stuck and angry. She accepted her anger, not in a passive or detached way of accepting the intolerable, but in a fully engaged way to channel her emotions and engage with this difficulty.

Having studied Sociology modules at university, Ali recognised the systemic nature of racism which lies behind police brutality. She knew that real change cannot occur unless the system changes. For Ali, this meant starting from early children's educational experiences. Through her social media networks, she linked up with two other young Black women whom she'd never met before, but she recognised in them a similar energy and refusal to accept the situation. Within just three short days they had worked together to arrange a Black Lives Matter protest in central London. 10,000 people attended! It was a peaceful, purposeful, angry, sad and empowering day. There were people of every colour in the crowds representing all of London. After the demonstration Ali and her two co-organisers made three demands: first, justice for Black people and people of colour who have died as a result of brutality or racism; second, more teaching on anti-racism within the education system; and third, redistribution of 10 per cent of the police budget towards community projects for young Black people and people of colour.

Explanation

This story of Ali's response to a difficulty shows the true meaning of acceptance, which is to take hold of or understand something. This enabled her to respond skilfully to the situation. Williams and Penman (2011) say that mindful acceptance 'gives us choices'. However, exploring difficulty is hard, and many people do not want to go towards their difficulties. Nevertheless, mindfulness teaches us that we need to learn to live with the things in our lives that are difficult rather than try to suppress them and pretend they are not there. Mindfulness will help you to take small steps towards accepting difficulty, and it enables you to come to see even the most difficult things in life as a process. You can learn to tune in to the physical reactions in your body to difficulty and develop an awareness of the changes of your body's responses to difficulties. Sometimes you might feel tense, or you may have a headache or stomach-ache. You may experience different feelings, such as a strong heart rate, sweating or a hot flush. Try to notice your physical reaction and maintain a gentle, compassionate awareness. If you can stay with those feelings for a moment, they will subside or change, and with this comes an awareness that change within the way you *think* about these difficulties is also possible. This will enable you to step back mentally and give you space to respond to the difficulty.

The well-known Austrian psychologist and Holocaust survivor, Viktor Frankl, whose work centres on the search for meaning as the motivation for life said:

"Between stimulus and response there is a space. That space is our power to choose our response. In our response lies our growth and our freedom."

Frankl's book *Man's Search for Meaning* (1946/2006) recounts his experiences in concentration camps during the Second World War. He describes the importance of maintaining his ability to determine his response to the atrocities around him and says that this enabled him to find some meaning in his circumstances. Frankl found that by helping other prisoners in the concentration camp, he was able to move from feelings of helplessness and meaninglessness to find a sense of dignity. This for him was the difference between life and death in the camps. Although his experience of the horror of concentration camps is extreme, in his professional life as a psychologist, after the war, he applied this theory to people struggling with depression. He developed therapeutic approaches with a focus on supporting patients with severe depression to find their own meaning in life.

After seeing footage of George Floyd's murder and the riots in America, Ali was able to pause and be with her feelings. With time she recognised that she had a choice between reacting impulsively with anger, reacting passively with inertia and hopelessness, or responding in a way that would help her to come closer to her desired outcome, which was positive action and social change. Through mindfulness practice Ali had been developing the muscle of attention. This enabled her to recognise the messages of her body and thoughts and have a sense of choice over whether to follow those messages or not. For Ali to have come to the point where she could take a pause and recognise that she had a choice about what action to take next, brings us to the core of mindfulness practice. This is the point that all the practices so far have been leading up to. This chapter's practice takes us a step closer to gaining some control over our reactions, particularly our thoughts. By gaining control we are able to get our reactions to work for us rather than direct us.

The stress response

A main element in the stress response in the brain is the *amygdala*, an almond-shaped part of the brain that is the brain's alarm system. It takes in signals from the body or the environment which indicate threat. When the amygdala interprets something as a threat, it sends a signal to the *hypothalamus* (a small region at the base of the brain which plays several crucial functions, including hormone release and temperature regulation). This triggers the *pituitary gland* to release chemicals such as adrenaline and cortisol which turn into the stress response, signalling to the entire body through the bloodstream to prepare for fight, flight or freeze.

- In *fight* mode, the body tenses and hardens the muscles so that we can fight, making our breathing more rapid so that we take in more oxygen.
- In *flight* mode, it speeds up the heartbeat to increase blood flow so that we can run.
- In *freeze* mode, our body closes down our digestive system to preserve energy, often closing down the system altogether so we feel frozen and unable to act.

The stress response turns down our relationship with the *hippocampus*, that part of the brain which lays down memory and is vitally important for study. As we have evolved as a species, we have developed a higher functioning part of the brain, the *prefrontal cortex*. This separates us from other mammals and enables us to think and have awareness of this. The prefrontal cortex helps us to make executive functioning decisions and time travel, enabling us to predict the future and remember the past. These functions help us to plan and create and regulate our thoughts, but they can also create worries.

The amygdala is closely connected to the prefrontal cortex. When all is functioning well, the prefrontal cortex can calm down the amygdala and prevent the stress response when it is not needed. However, when the stress response has already been activated, contact with the prefrontal cortex is severed and we cannot reason with ourselves to calm down. Instead, we either find it difficult to think or we run into a negative spiral of thoughts which feed the stress response. When this happens, we need to find a way to calm our system down and regulate our minds and bodies to reconnect us to our prefrontal cortex. This soothing function is done by the *parasympathetic nervous system*, which is responsible for the body's rest and relaxation, allowing the body to calm down after a stressful situation.

When the human stress response evolved, it was in response to the mortal threat of death from predators or it signalled that we were suffering from an internal injury. This system was created for extreme physical stress, so it is not surprising that it closes down our thinking function so that we track only for physical threat tuning into sounds and sensations which keep us hyper-alert to threat. Therefore, the stress response is a very useful survival mechanism for prehistoric man but not always ideal in humans' contemporary circumstances. Today, we are prone to many stressors which we interpret as a threat to our sense of self. The amygdala can be likened to a smoke alarm; when it detects a real threat or fire, the alarm system can save our lives. However, the smoke alarm can be triggered at any time by the tiniest detection of smoke, such as burning toast. This is annoying and we have to spend a lot of time trying to cool the kitchen down, opening doors and fanning the alarm. The whole episode can deregulate our system and turn the simple act of making toast into a festival of adrenaline and cortisol. Thus, it can shift a calm mood into one of agitation which can be difficult to dislodge.

Mindfulness techniques can help us to prevent the body's alarm system being triggered, or it enables us to respond to it with a pause which allows us to keep connected to our logical, mindfulness-mind. This is done by breathing or naming the agitation and soothing it, rather than moving into a full-blown stress response of fight, flight or freeze. However, when the body and mind are exposed to continual threats, the system can never really calm down; instead, it keeps hyper-alert to signs of further stress or indeed mis-identifies signals so we are constantly running on low-level stress and reacting with anxiety or panic. Very often when we panic our minds can start interpreting everything in a negative way. The thoughts we need to be especially vigilant towards are described by Williams and Penman (2011) as indicators of high anxiety and depression. These four indicators are:

- **Catastrophic thinking:** In this style of thinking, for example, students might convince themselves that if they don't get a first-class honours degree, they will end up working in a dead-end job with no prospects.
- **Irreversibility:** Adopting this style of thinking, students might believe that if their last assignment was marked down, they will never get a good mark again.
- **Painful engagement:** With this style of thinking, students might ruminate over something in their mind and pepper it with 'what ifs': 'What if people think I am stupid or prejudiced?' 'What if they do not want me to join their discussion again?'
- **Over-generalisation:** This style of thinking is associated with thoughts such as: 'I never get to keep friends; they always find someone who is better than me'.

If Ali had let herself fall into any of these thought patterns, she might have sunk into helplessness and depression and not have been able to see the power and possibility in her thoughts and actions to make constructive change. This chapter, especially the part about confronting difficulty, illustrates one concept from mindfulness - that we can't avoid pain, but do have a choice about suffering. Buddhism describes pain using three arrows:

- Pain is the first arrow whether that be physical or emotional and can't really be avoided as a human being
- Suffering, resisting, bracing against the pain is the second arrow
- The third arrow is allowing our thoughts to hate or be angry with it and fight against it.

Many authors have embraced this idea. In *What I Talk About When I Talk About Running*, Murakami (2009) describes the pain one often experiences when running. He says, 'Pain is inevitable. Suffering is optional.' This is a very useful concept to bear in mind when you experience a painful situation.

Practice: Sitting Meditation

This chapter introduces the heart of the mindfulness practice: the Sitting Meditation. Though known as the Sitting Meditation, like all the mindfulness exercises you can find your own comfortable position and you can practise it lying down if you find that more comfortable. It is important to bring kindness to yourself. It begins with a brief settling with the body, before going into mindfulness of breath and body, then focusing on sounds and thoughts.

Sounds

This involves focusing our awareness on the sounds around us and, as best we can, simply receiving them without preference. By doing this we recognise the sounds as mental activity which enter into our consciousness when we give our attention to them. It is important to stress that we are not straining to hear, trying to hunt for sounds, thinking about them or analysing them. We simply tune in to what sounds are actually arising, fading, mingling, orchestrating or pouncing into our ear receptors at this moment.

Sounds can create an emotional reaction in us. Some sounds, such as interruptions or the sounds of traffic, trigger a sense of judgement, which makes us want to push the sounds away. Other sounds, such as running water or birdsong, soothe or please us. These sounds give us a sense of calm and we want more of them. We notice how sounds can change a mood from annoyance or anxiety to peace and wellbeing. During this exercise we work at observing sounds as best we can, but not reacting to them. Interestingly, it is said that Buddhist monks and nuns can remain in a state of meditation even when surrounded by disturbing sounds. However, if any of these sounds suggest danger of some sort, the monks and nuns are able to recognise that and respond accordingly. So, the exercise sharpens our awareness rather than dampens it.

Thoughts

We then move from sounds into actually observing the pattern of thoughts as they arise into our awareness. Within this practice, we notice the nature of these thoughts – are they worries, plans, criticisms, daydreams? At this point, we do our best to allow the thoughts to arise without judgement and then move on. Let us use the analogy of our minds as the grey road and our thoughts as big, red double-decker buses. So, in our heads, over and over again, we choose not to get on the bus. When we find ourselves lost in thought, we congratulate ourselves for noticing this and get off the bus and go back to just observing our thoughts as they go past.

We can extend the repertoire of our metaphors to seeing thoughts as characters who walk across the stage or screen of our minds. We watch them pass by and then watch them walk off stage. When we find ourselves engaging with these characters, we do our best to de-couple ourselves from them and come back to observing the empty stage. In Buddhist meditation, clouds are often used to represent thoughts. Some clouds appear heavy and dense and seem to consume us. Other thoughts, in contrast, are so light and wispy we can hardly catch their content. Like all clouds, they will eventually pass, so we understand that thoughts are no more our mind than clouds are the clear blue sky. They are atmospheric conditions, which, if left alone, will eventually pass. But, if we allow them to take a hold, they will have control over our moods and can turn into debilitating ruminations or intrusive thoughts that will not leave us alone.

The point of this exercise is to realise that, like sounds, thoughts are mental activity. On a Magnetic Resonance Imaging (MRI) brain scan they can be seen as little neural firings which can quickly take a hold and cascade into neural nets. These can take us down well-trodden, debilitating or overwhelming thought pathways, such as 'I'm not good enough', or 'nobody likes me'. However, using mindfulness practice we can find a place of power that we have been developing by consistently bringing our attention back again and again.

This enables us to catch negative thoughts before they take a hold and let them pass by. In this way, we begin to appreciate that 'thoughts are not facts' (Kabat-Zinn, 2013). An important but difficult message of mindfulness is that although some thoughts may be true, self-critical thoughts rarely are. They are subjective and transitory, which means that we can change them or change the way we think about them. This gives us the power to take control and develop more positive ways of seeing our thoughts.

We also begin to notice that some thoughts are associated with an emotional trigger. For example, the thought of an exam or a deadline can bring with it a tightening of the stomach, a quickening of the heart or a tensing of the shoulders. These physical sensations indicate dread or anxiety. But if we drop into the body and notice the physical manifestation of an emotion, we can start to see it less like a thief threatening to rob us of our equilibrium, and more like a familiar sensation which arises from within us and will dissipate if we allow ourselves to let it pass. Emotions are sometimes led from a thought and sometimes precede a thought, but they are intrinsically linked. We can step back from emotions if we realise that they don't have to control us, or we can listen to them and wisely choose the next best thought or action. Just like sounds, we learn that being able to discern useful thoughts from destructive ones gives us power and focus. And, like sounds, managing thoughts does not numb them, but in fact makes them work more efficiently for us.

Meditation: Body and Breath, Sounds and Thoughts

Body: Settle into a comfortable position with your legs uncrossed, your feet connected to the floor and your eyes closed or relaxed. Bring your awareness to physical sensations by focusing your attention on the sensations of touch in the body, where it is in contact with the floor and with whatever you are sitting or lying on. Spend a few moments exploring these sensations.

Now, focusing your attention on your feet, starting with the toes, expand the 'spotlight of attention' so it takes in the soles of your feet, the heels and the top of your feet, until you are attending to any and all of the physical sensations you become aware of in both feet, moment by moment. Spend a few moments attending to the feet in this way, noticing how sensations arise and dissolve in awareness. If there are no sensations in this region of the body, simply register a blank. This is perfectly fine – you are not trying to make sensations happen – you are simply registering what is already here when you attend.

Now, expand your attention to take in the rest of both legs for a few moments, then the torso (from the pelvis and hips up to the shoulders); then the left arm; then the right arm; then the neck and head.

Spend a minute or two resting in the awareness of the whole body. See if it is possible to allow your body and its sensations to be just as you find them. Explore how it is to let go of the tendency to want things to be a certain way. Even one brief moment of seeing how things are – without wanting to change anything – can be profoundly nourishing.

Breath: Now bring your awareness to the breath as it moves in and out of the body at the abdomen. Notice the changing patterns of physical sensations in this region of the body as the breath moves in and out. It may help to place your hand here for a few breaths, and feel the abdomen rising and falling. Or use one of the alternatives, opening and closing your hand, or feeling your body against a surface.

You may notice mild sensations of stretching as the abdomen gently rises with each inbreath, and different sensations as the abdomen falls with each outbreath. As best you can, follow closely with your attention, so you notice the changing physical sensations for the full duration of each inbreath and the full duration of each outbreath, perhaps noticing the slight pauses between one inbreath and the following outbreath, and between one outbreath and the following inbreath.

Sounds: Now focus your attention on hearing. You might be able to hear sounds from near or far, in front of you or behind, to the sides, above or below ... Notice if you label the sounds or judge them in any way. Notice how some sounds make you think of stories to tell yourself. Some sounds you will find pleasant, others rather annoying. Try to hear the rhythm, pitch and feel of the sounds. Some sounds might be hidden by more prominent sounds. As you listen, you might detect a quieter space between sounds. Be aware of the space in which sounds arise.

Thoughts: Now bring your awareness to your thoughts. Don't try to control your thoughts; instead, allow them to come and go like clouds across your mind. Try not to judge your thoughts – just observe them, sometimes dark sometimes light, sometimes funny, sometimes sad ... But with all of these different clouds, the sky remains the same.

Try to see your thoughts as events arising in the mind and dispersing. Be aware of any emotions that do arise, and try to be open to them no matter what they are. Be aware if your mind gets caught up in thoughts. Try to disentangle yourself from those thoughts and go back to your breath and an awareness of the present moment ... Always use the breath as an anchor to return to your thoughts.

For the last few moments of this meditation, come back to focusing on your breathing. Remember that wherever you are, the breath is always there to bring you back into the moment. Then, when you are ready, slowly open your eyes and return your attention to the group.

Reflection: Unpleasant events/difficulties

Take a few minutes to bring a difficulty to mind. After anchoring yourself in the present moment through the breath you can explore bringing to mind a small difficulty, perhaps one linked to an unpleasant event you experienced during the week. At this point, it is best to bring to mind a simple difficulty, an annoyance or frustration, a minor disappointment, not something too big at this early stage of practice. You can explore the issue of stress by looking at the feedback from the unpleasant events diary, which helps you to recognise the mechanisms of stress. By enquiring into this exercise, you can begin to notice the components of unpleasant experiences in the body, emotions and thoughts. You will also notice those automatic habits of responding to stress; crying, hiding away, taking alcohol or drugs, eating sugary foods and so on. This enables you to differentiate between the components of an unpleasant experience and realise that if you practise a breathing space at the point of stress, you can choose the best response, which might be to distract yourself or maybe take a closer look. This develops our 'window of tolerance' (Siegel, 2020) for dealing with distress and responding rather than reacting. You can then imagine the situation in your mind's eye.

Williams and Penman (2011) talk about bringing the difficulty onto the 'workbench of our mind'. The aim is to bring the situation into our consciousness so that you can explore how it affects the body. This entails leaving the story and the thoughts behind and dropping into the body. When you do this, you will notice how it feels – a heaviness in the shoulders, a tightness in the chest or a clenching of the hands. Naturally, the mind will want to get involved so that it can analyse the situation and it can drown us in some very thick clouds and turbulent thoughts. This is where the discipline of your practice comes in and you allow the thoughts to pass. You can come back to an awareness of the physical sensations, gently allowing them to be there but softening and soothing them just like in the body scan. This is a practice of uncoupling from the mind and letting your thoughts be. It helps by not increasing the thoughts through resistance and unnecessary tensing.

Although counterintuitive, you will realise that facing these sensations with curiosity rather than bracing against them results in a kind of power and ease. This is a good way of being able to manage your thoughts. Cultivating the attitude of curiosity and kindness over the past few weeks will have provided the foundation for being compassionate towards yourself. This can free you from those habitual defensive patterns you can fall into which tend to further entrench you into the stress response. You can hold yourself in deep kindness even when you have made a mistake. This enables you to look at what is actually happening and not fall prey to assumptions and automatic pilot reactions.

It is useful to remember in mindfulness that we do not ask why; this is the territory of counsellors and therapists. It is also what we do when we over-analyse ourselves, which can tie the mind in to all sorts of debilitating knots. Instead, in mindfulness we ask: where, what, how, when? This gives us a direct connection to how our stress and all of our emotions manifest in the body. In this way, we can begin to step away from them; not by detaching, but by acknowledging and reviewing. Therefore, we can gain some autonomy over our reactions by recognising that emotions are a cluster of physical sensations which we define with our thoughts.

To date, we have been looking at our different triggers to stress coming from our bodies, memories and our interpretations of the environment. It is now time to look more closely at what happens in our bodies and brains when we experience stress.

Lesson Plan: Session 4

Session aim: To work with thoughts and gain some control

Objectives:
1. Practise separating thoughts from reactions
2. Learn about the stress response
3. Learn to take an intentional pause before reacting

Activities:	Time:
1. Body and Breath, Sounds and Thoughts Meditation	20 minutes
2. Enquiry	15 minutes
3. Feedback from unpleasant events diary	15 minutes
4. Feedback from moving meditation and body scan practice	10 minutes
5. Explain the stress response	10 minutes
6. Discussion: How do you react to stress?	10 minutes
7. Read 'Exam in 5 Ways' and discuss	10 minutes

Notes:
1. The meditation for this week can be slightly longer because students are by now becoming more used to mindfulness practice.
2. As usual, spend time asking students for feedback on the meditation practice.
   - What did they notice?
   - What thoughts came up?
   - Which sounds were positive?
   - Which were negative?
   - How did naming the thought or sound change their association with it?
3. As students report unpleasant events, get them to focus on what they noticed in their body.
4. Students will be becoming more familiar with regular mindfulness practice now, so gather feedback about what they are noticing as they develop their practice.
5. The stress response: developed in the brain by stressful events in life. At the sign of stress the amygdala interprets the event as stressful, which sends a signal to the body to trigger the stress response, meaning preparing the body for fight, flight or freeze.
6. What is your defence mechanism when you are stressed? Do you want to eat chocolate? Do you cry? Do you withdraw? Do you fight? Do you drink/use drugs? Can you interrupt this defensive habit by stepping back from events for a moment to make a choice that is wise for you?
7. This poem focuses on the stress of exams which is something that all students can relate to, even if they no longer have to sit exams.

Homework:
- This week try to notice how stress manifests in the body; what happens emotionally and in your thoughts?
- Practise the Body and Breath, Sounds and Thoughts Meditation four or five times in the week
- Practise the Breathing Space Meditation whenever you feel the need to

The stress response

The brain tracks for threat or closes down altogether in order to give blood and oxygen to the rest of the body. These days the stress response is rarely triggered by life-threatening events; instead, it is usually triggered by a threat to our sense of self – that is, not revising enough, not getting the results we think we need, etc. What happens to the brain when the amygdala has signalled that there is a threat? The more active the amygdala is, the less active the hippocampus is, where we hold our memory and our prefrontal cortex, where we make our best and wisest decisions. Thus, when we feel stressed, we can't remember things, and our mind either becomes overactive with ruminating thoughts or seems to freeze or can't remember at all. Not a good situation when sitting an exam.

The most difficult thoughts we have that can lead to anxiety/depression are:

1 Catastrophic thinking
2 Irreversibility
3 Painful engagement
4 Over-generalised thinking

Mindfulness enables you to pause when you feel stressed and do the 3-minute breathing space.

Exam in 5 Ways

(based on the poem 'Autobiography in five short chapters': Portia Nelson)

1 I sit down at the desk.
   There is a question on the paper I didn't expect.
   I panic.
   I am lost … I am hopeless.
   It isn't my fault.
   It takes forever to start to think straight.

2 I sit down at the same desk.
   There is a question on the paper I didn't expect.
   I pretend I don't see it.
   I panic again.
   I can't believe I'm in the same place.
   But it isn't my fault.
   It still takes a long time to think straight.

3 I sit down at the same desk.
   There is a question on the paper I didn't expect.
   I see it is there.
   I still panic … it's a habit.
   My eyes are open.
   I know where I am.

It is my fault.
I breathe deeply and re-read the question.

4 I sit down at the same desk
There is a question on the paper I didn't expect.
I leave it and read the next question.

5 I come back to the question and I realise I can begin to answer it!

References

Frankl, V. (2006) *Man's Search for Meaning: An Introduction to Logotherapy.* Boston, MA: Beacon Press (originally published 1946).

Kabat-Zinn, J. (2013) *Full Catastrophe Living: How to Cope with Stress, Pain and Illness Using Mindfulness Meditation.* London: Piatkus Books.

Murakami, H. (2009) *What I Talk about When I Talk about Running.* New York: Vintage.

Siegel, D. (2020) *The Developing Mind: How Relationships and the Brain Interact to Shape Who We Are,* 3rd edition. New York: Guilford Press.

Williams, M. and Penman, D. (2011) *Mindfulness: A Practical Guide to Finding Peace in a Frantic World.* London: Piatkus Books.

5 Integrating mindfulness into life

Eliot's story

Eliot is in the second year of his Environmental Studies degree. He is a very conscientious and talented student with a strong commitment to environmental issues and is actively involved in various eco-groups. Eliot has ADHD, which means he has lots of energy and a great ability to see widely and creatively and to make connections others don't obviously make. The difficult side of his ADHD is a hyper-sensitivity to other people's feelings. He can get distracted trying to help them or just by their noise or moods. Giving out so much energy often leaves him overwhelmed because all the parts of his life collide and he gets exhausted from running on adrenaline. This often results in him having to hide himself away and retreat in order to regulate and re-fuel himself.

As the deadlines and exams crept up, so did Eliot's anxiety levels, which exacerbated his ADHD symptoms. His studies required him to read about the critical state of the world's environment and the impending climate crisis, but he felt helpless to respond. The eco-groups he was involved in were going through a slightly disorganised period, causing frustration for everyone. For Eliot the level of confusion and the unclear communication channels left him feeling agitated and exhausted. He was finding it hard to remain connected to the various eco-groups. He couldn't cope with the high energy and chaos of the groups, so felt a profound sense of meaninglessness and isolation.

On top of this, one of Eliot's housemates had gone through a recent break-up and needed a lot of support. He leant on Eliot a lot, which Eliot felt he just could not refuse. As a result, Eliot became overwhelmed, falling behind in his work, feeling anxious and exhausted with no sense of purpose. His only way to cope was to shut himself away and distract himself with games and books. This meant that he became more and more isolated. He was unable to concentrate or focus, and he was falling into familiar patterns of procrastination.

Before this, Eliot had been attending mindfulness sessions for some time and he had been finding it very useful. However, as often happens when people get stressed, he felt he did not have time to do the things which most sustained him. Eliot stopped attending the weekly sessions and abandoned his daily mindfulness practice. However, he bumped into another member of the mindfulness society who persuaded him to attend a mindfulness drop-in. Eliot went and there he was reminded of five things which are the focus of this chapter:

1 *Practise loving kindness to yourself*
2 *Connect self, friends and family*

3 *Exchange self-criticism for self-compassion*

4 *Recognise and accept who you are and how you function best*

5 *Identify strategies to employ when you feel your mental health or coping strategies slipping.*

Explanation: Practise loving kindness to yourself

This chapter is all about acceptance and finding how mindfulness practice works best for you. The Loving Kindness Meditation, taken from Buddhist traditions, has been seen to have extensive benefits for oneself, our relationships with others and the planet. The first part of loving kindness, bringing compassion to ourselves, is most valuable for young students because at this stage of life people are often judgemental and critical of themselves and feel deficient in some way. As your mindfulness practice develops, you can go deeper and use the whole of the 'metta meditation', which has five different phases. The first is sending compassion to self, then to a benefactor or loved one, next to an acquaintance, then to someone with whom you experience a difficulty and, finally, to all sentient beings. This level of loving kindness can be done with students who chose to go deeper with their mindfulness practice and have continued to meditate for some time.

Loving kindness practice has been studied closely by the neuroscientist, Richard Davidson. A meditator for over 40 years, he was one of the founders of the 'Healthy Minds Project' (see below in the resources section for a link). After meeting the Dalai Lama in 1992, he dedicated his research to the study of meditation on the brain. In the book *Altered Traits* with Daniel Goleman (Goleman and Davidson, 2017), he recalls a challenge the Dalai Lama set him to use neuroscience to promote the cultivation of kindness and compassion rather than to understand fear, anxiety and depression. He says that this was a total 'wake-up call'. Goleman and Davidson assert that mindfulness has many benefits including developing empathy and moving us away from our own self-centred thoughts. These changes can happen from just an 8 week mindfulness course.

As humans we are unique; we all have things that we are good at and enjoy, but we also have insecurities and self-doubt. The story for this chapter highlights ADHD, which falls into a larger group of terms that are collectively known as 'neurodiversity'. Neurodiversity takes into account variations in the human brain regarding learning, mood, attention, sociability and other mental functions. The term neurodiversity does not pathologise the conditions, meaning they are not regarded as abnormal or unhealthy but they are viewed as differences to be understood and worked with. As in any large organisation, many university staff and students are neurodiverse. Conditions include dyslexia, dyspraxia, dyscalculia, ADHD and autism.

Alongside the social and behavioural differences that neurodiverse people can find challenging, many exhibit great strengths and qualities, including: environmental activist Greta Thunberg, who calls Asperger's her 'superpower'; the founder of Apple, Steve Jobs; scientist Albert Einstein and poet Emily Dickinson.

(For more information on well-known neurodiverse people, see the link below in the resources section.) Although the world is reliant on and indeed has been progressed by people who are neurodiverse, many institutions and education systems are not equipped to be inclusive of such individuals. Therefore, coping with this can cause significant social and mental health issues for people who do not feel they fit in.

Mindfulness teaches loving kindness and this starts with the self. Once you can accept yourself with loving kindness (even the parts of yourself which you are insecure about), you can then begin to extend loving kindness to others, starting with those closest to you and extending out to people who you encounter briefly and even people you don't know. This mindset of loving kindness is a core part of mindfulness practice.

Connection

Loving Kindness Meditation can produce a much greater sense of our connection to ourselves, others, other species and our planet as a whole. As Loving Kindness Meditation is one of the ways we can address the climate crisis and toxic divisions over materialism, so it spoke to Eliot in a very direct way. (For further reading on this topic, see *The Self Delusion* 2020 by Tom Oliver.) Oliver cites scientific evidence from many of the major scientific schools, psychology and philosophy to show how the idea that we are separate entities in the world is delusional. He contends that we are all interconnected, not just within our own bodies, but with others, all species and the fauna and flora of our planet. He argues that our obsession with individualism and the delusion of separateness allows us to objectify each other, other animals and the planet and has resulted in unprecedented rises in loneliness, depression and anxiety. He says,

> "it's a cruel twist of irony that the advent of information technology in the modern world is coincident with rising levels of mental health disorder, including anxiety, depression and self-harm."
>
> (Oliver, 2020: 222)

Although technology is undoubtedly a useful way to promote connection, it can also be a barrier to making real connections with the people you are with. Many students are very dependent on their phones and social media to facilitate social life, but mindfulness teaches the importance of creating balance in life, and this can be extended to social connections, which can be online but must also be real. The Loving Kindness Meditation reminds us of the power of connection and that we all have the ability to increase our sense of connection with ourselves, so that we are more compassionate to ourselves and more accepting of who we are – with all our diverse and unique attributes.

Exchange self-criticism for self-compassion

Mindfulness teaches self-compassion as a way to look after ourselves and meet our own needs. It is common for us to focus on our perceived shortcomings, but this can be debilitating and lead to anxiety. In terms of study, this is very important; many students place pressure themselves to achieve excellence or to meet deadlines, even when they are experiencing difficult personal issues. This adds to stress and ultimately is counter-productive to academic work because it distracts students from focusing on their assignments. Negative feedback on assignments or low marks can sometimes lead students to ruminate negatively on their studies, which can undermine their confidence and decrease motivation, so whilst it is important to take feedback on board, it is also vital to be kind to yourself so that you can focus positively on your next assignment.

Eliot had a regular mindfulness practice, but he had let it slip when life got busy. This had a negative impact on his wellbeing and on his academic work. However, on returning to the mindfulness group, he was able to recognise that the long, eyes-closed meditations were not easy for him. The session he attended was on Loving Kindness Meditation and he began to remember that feeling overwhelmed is nothing to be ashamed of, which had been happening to him. When Eliot focused on what he most needed rather than punishing himself for 'failing', he began to feel some compassion for that part of himself which felt overwhelmed. When he feels in any way agitated or burdened with over-thinking, it is better for Eliot to do some of the informal practices such as coming into the moment with a breathing space or just coming into a pause and tuning into the moment by checking his senses. Checking your senses is a good way to take a moment. You can do this by feeling the touch of the ground beneath your feet, looking at your surroundings, listening to the sounds present where you are, and smelling and tasting the moment.

Eliot needed to tune into the things which nourish and sustain him and recognise that when life is hectic. He really needs to practise acceptance of his ADHD. He realised that he needed to cut back on the things which deplete him and, where possible, increase the things that nourish him. From the 'pleasant event' activity in Chapter 2, he remembered that nourishing activities do not need to be big things. In fact, small bursts of pleasure in seeing, hearing, feeling and tasting could create little surges of serotonin. For example, just having the motivation to walk a short distance could give him some dopamine and endorphins, and if he managed to connect with a dog, a bird or another human being, he could generate enough oxytocin to combat further stress hormones.

For Eliot, the reminder of bringing compassion to himself and adjusting his expectations of himself and others helped him a great deal. He could reflect on the things which were really draining him and identify some clear boundaries so that he could support himself better. In that way, he could preserve his energy so that he could cope with his life and his values and activism in a way that worked for him. This allowed him to stay active and engaged for longer periods of time.

Practice: Acceptance

Understanding who we are and how to work with our uniqueness can allow us to be most effective in the world. When we know who we are and are comfortable with our identity, it is possible to 'own a label' with pride and claim all the extraordinary gifts which go with it. It was very painful for Eliot to take in all the information that he was learning on his course about the environmental crises. His activism had helped him to feel some kind of hope and power. However, being a part of an organisation meant dealing with many different energies and people. There was some conflict and quite a lot of disorganisation and unpredictability. Such a combination is difficult for many people with varying kinds of neurodiversity. And because of Eliot's high sense of morality, it was debilitating for him to lose his connection to activism. As life became more overwhelming, he felt swamped and isolated. When Eliot was feeling stressed, the noise and chaos of the activist groups made it important for him to step away. This break helped him to regain a sense of balance so that when his friend encouraged him back to mindfulness, he felt able to reconnect with it. This reminded him of the strategies which help him to function best.

Pacing ourselves and looking at the habitual ways we have of coping with shame or overwhelm is really useful, so we can decide if our automatic pilot mechanism really serves or hinders us. When we accept who we are, our gifts and our limitations, we can begin to be more protective towards ourselves. We can also identify some clear boundaries when we feel ourselves becoming dys-regulated or overwhelmed. One of the tenets of Loving Kindness Meditation is bringing some acceptance and compassion to who we are and the gifts and limitations of our lives. This enables us to recognise the things we cannot change about ourselves and society – and the things that we can. This well-known prayer reminds us of this fact.

"Lord, give me courage to change what must be altered,

Serenity to accept what cannot be helped,

And insight to know one from the other."

(Reinhold Niebuhr, 1892–1971)

Meditation: Loving Kindness

Settle as fully as you can into this moment. Start with adopting a sense of kindness towards yourself. Find a comfortable position, either lying down or sitting in a chair, with your legs uncrossed, bringing a sense of gentle aware-ness to your experience of this moment. Bring your awareness to your five senses in the here and now.

As you settle, perhaps take a gentle look at the things around you: the everyday things of the room and the surroundings. Just allow yourself to notice the light, the shapes, the colours without straining or labelling. Then, if you are comfort-able with this, perhaps you can close your eyes or have a gentle gaze just ahead of you. As you do this, the other senses might become a little more vivid.

Gently allow your senses to open up to the soundscape around you. Not seeking sounds, but just being awake to the sounds coming towards you –

inside and outside of your body, above, below and to the sides of you. These can be gentle, familiar sounds which suddenly appear centre-stage: the ticking of the clock, the sound of the radiator and sounds which may suddenly appear, linger for a while and then disappear. Sounds that are inside the room and outside the room. Some sounds are soothing, like bird song, and some jarring, such as a revving car engine. Try to simply notice the sounds rather than judge them.

Gently move your attention to taste and smell: the familiar smell of your room or the smell of fresh air. Taste any residue flavours of food or drinks you have had which still register in your mouth.

Then move to the sensation of touch. Start by tuning into any contact your body has with the surface supporting you. Perhaps this is the sense of your head resting against a pillow, or your buttocks and thighs as they touch the seat of the chair. Move your attention to the places in your body where you can feel some tightness or heaviness; perhaps at your jaw, allowing it to fall open a little. The important thing with these little movements of release or stretch is that we bring momentary awareness to what we are doing. Gently focus your awareness on your neck; would you like to move it slightly from side to side? Or would you like to move your shoulders gently up and down? Do all of this with kind intent to bring greater ease to your body. Now extend your awareness to your back, your arms and your throat. On the way, notice the places you are bracing and gently breathe into these areas with kind awareness. On the outbreath gently release any tension either with a small movement or by imagining you can let go of any bracing that you don't really need.

Now move your awareness to the soles of your feet. What, if anything, can you feel? If your mind is suddenly in charge of your attention and leading you onto a thought cloud or you are deep in conversation with a character walking across the stage of your mind, try not to judge yourself – it's okay, that's what minds do. Congratulate yourself for noticing and with as much kindness and firmness as you can muster, escort your attention back to being with the toes of both feet. Notice if they are warm or cold; maybe you can't feel anything – that is fine too.

Now move your attention, like the beam of a torch, to the area of your tummy, your digestive system. Can you feel anything here? Any tightness, fullness or emptiness? Allow your attention to move all the way to the area of your shoulders and arms and down to the fingertips. Just notice any or no sensations of ease or tightness, cool or warmth that you feel. Then lead your attention up to the area of your head and face. Gently glide your attention to any furrowing on your forehead or pulsing at the temples, tightness in the cheeks or jaw. Scan your whole face and, where you find a sense of tension or discomfort, perhaps imagine that you can breathe into this area with the inbreath and on the outbreath soothe, release and let go.

Then, gently come up close to the feeling of your breath as it moves in and out of your nose or mouth. Harness the sense of the breath if you like by taking a deep quick breath in where you feel the cool air coming in through your nostrils and a long breath out feeling the warm breath leaving through your mouth. After a couple of breaths, allow your breath to breathe itself in its own rhythm and with your attention, see if you can follow one whole inbreath as it moves through your nose and windpipe and lifts your chest and belly and the whole outbreath as your belly and chest recede. Just be with your breath for a few moments.

Option 1. Gently begin to bring this meditation to an end, without any rush, in your own time. Wiggle your fingers and toes and maybe have a little stretch and when you are ready, open your eyes and congratulate yourself for having taken this time to actively work on your own physical, mental and emotional wellbeing.

Option 2. Loving kindness: Bring your attention to the area of your heart. If you are comfortable doing this, put the palm of your hand over your heart and gently let it rest there. Bring your warm, appreciative attention to all the work that the heart does to keep you alive and all the emotions it holds and which emerge when you are feeling sad or excited; fearful or courageous; despairing or joyful. And just allow your heart and your nervous system to rest for a while, feeling safe with a warm feeling of belonging; nothing to do and nowhere to go. Perhaps bring to mind a sense of feeling absolutely loved and enough ... A sense of really accepting yourself – even your mistakes and believing in your good intent. Sometimes it's hard to remember a time when we felt accepted like this without conditions. The best way to find it is to think of the unconditional love of a pet or to just imagine for a moment what that might feel like ... A sense of real acceptance that we are doing the best we can ... And in this space say silently to yourself:

May I be safe,
May I be happy,
May I be well,
May I be free from suffering,
May I come to love and accept all that I am,
May I live with ease,
May I know joy.

Allow these words to really sink in and repeat them a couple of times. (Invite participants to include any other wishes they might want or need at this time. Then repeat the loving kindness to the group.)

May you be safe,
May you be happy,
May you be well,
May you be free from suffering,
May you come to love and accept all that you are,
May you live with ease,
May you know joy.
Then gently return your attention to the breath and slowly come out of the meditation.

It is important to note that this meditation can be quite emotional for some people, as it's hard for them to remember or imagine feeling unconditional love, or they feel guilty for wishing these things for themselves. It is here that we can normalise this and reassure participants that bringing loving kindness to themselves is the best way to take responsibility when they need to. This will help them not to get defensive because we need to bring loving kindness to ourselves first and then it's so much easier to bring loving kindness to others.

Reflection: Nourishing/depleting activities

We all have different ways of doing things which work for us. For example, some people have straight-line thinking. They tend to collect and collate things in a linear, progressive way. This can be very useful for academic tasks such as structuring writing. Others have more circular, spiral thinking. They can collect and connect things in a cascading way but often find it difficult to contain it all. These are great creative skills, but they can be chaotic. Some people are drawn to the big picture, whereas others focus on details. A lot has been written about learning styles (Honey and Mumford, 2012) and personality types (Briggs Myers and Myers, 2010), so if you are interested to find out more, see some of the resources listed below. The important thing for mindfulness is to develop your own awareness of your strengths and practise compassion towards yourself for the things which you find more challenging.

Once you know yourself and your strengths and weaknesses, you can then make more confident and informed decisions about your life. This is important for students because they are faced with lots of decisions, many of which will have far-reaching implications for their lives ahead. This is why it is important to really think deeply about what is best for you. For example, at the end of the first year, students often need to decide which modules they will study in their second year. Then, in the second year, they are often asked to commit to a dissertation topic or extended project. Mindfulness can help with decision-making because it helps you to focus on the moment. In addition, its teaching of loving kindness will help you to make decisions that are right for you rather than decisions that will please your family or achieve goals that were not set by you.

Identify strategies to employ when you feel your mental health or coping strategies slipping

It is useful to develop your own strategies for when you might be feeling overwhelmed. Mindfulness practice teaches that it is always possible to come back to the anchor of the breath. For example, you can take a few moments to focus on following the breath in and out for six breaths. If you prefer, you can try mindful walking, movement or any form of exercise. The secret is that, in the moment, you are focusing intentionally on something within yourself or something in your environment. This means that you are tuning into the moment, not following your thoughts or transient distractions which try to pull you away. If you find it difficult to feel your breath, you can put your hand on your belly or chest to help you connect with your breath. You can count each inbreath and each outbreath. You can open your hand on the inbreath and close your hand on the outbreath. Alternatively, you can squeeze an expanding ball in your hand in time with your breath to keep focused. In addition, almost any everyday activity can be done mindfully – washing-up, colouring-in, dancing, running, cooking. All of these things can be mindful so long as you do the best you can to focus your attention on the activity, and you watch your mind and notice when your thoughts come, letting them pass by.

In addition to bringing mindfulness to your everyday activities, another way to develop coping strategies is to focus your attention on doing more of the activities in life which nourish you and minimise the time spent on depleting activities. Although we all have different activities that nourish or deplete us, there are things that regularly come up in discussion with students. Please feel free to add your own:

Nourishing activities	Depleting activities
• Walking or being in nature • Listening to music • Doing physical exercise • Taking a shower or bath	• Endless hours on your phone or other screen-based time • Eating junk food • Having circular arguments with friends/family • Not getting enough sleep/sleeping too much

Student perspective 3

"From a young age, I have had what could be called an excitable mind. Constant distraction was my normal state of being. I discovered meditation in my early teens. At first, I held the [common] misconception that meditation is an esoteric path reserved for sages and yogis to silence their minds. Of course, this is misleading. If anything, the essence of mindfulness is the complete opposite. I define mindfulness as the quality of staying fully present and engaged with whatever you are doing.

To me, this characterises mindfulness as the skill of all skills. One can bring mindfulness to any situation. Watching the breath. Washing dishes. Even in the middle of an argument. The integration of mindfulness in your life is only limited by your imagination. The cost is small, but the pay-off is immense. Though I try to have a formal sitting practice, I find that it is the more day-to-day applications of mindfulness that affect my life most profoundly. Restricting mindfulness to your meditation sessions is a wasted opportunity to bring more clarity to the broader narrative of your life.

For the longest time, meditation was something I practised in solitude. This changed when I joined the mindfulness society and the 8 week course. A supportive community always helps someone progress in a skill or a discipline, but it is especially beneficial in mindfulness. Sometimes, when practising alone, our patience and our compassion towards ourselves can seem contrived. A support group that allows you to share and contrast your experiences along the same path helps you overcome such obstacles.

I like to think of my mind as an ocean. Sometimes calm, sometimes turbulent. Always changing. Somewhere in this ocean is a ship. This ship is a symbol of my conscious intention. When I continuously battle my mind, the voyage becomes difficult. It is like sailing against a storm. Mindfulness is simply a way to strengthen the ship's capability to navigate the waters. Like an actual voyage, it is not about defeating the ocean. It is about understanding Her. Understanding the ebbs and flows of the mind with a genuine curiosity (and not with preconceived notions) is the best way to make it work in your favour. Bringing mindfulness into our lives helps us nudge our ships towards a course that is in service of our deepest inclinations." (Ijaz Aflah, Law student)

This chapter has looked at the things which nourish and deplete us (taken from MBSR/MBCT) and the tiny little actions and thoughts we can develop to help us increase our experience of nourishment and lessen the impact of the things which we find depleting. Often, we discover the reason for something being depleting or nourishing is our attitude towards it. The late Zen master and mindfulness teacher, Thich Nhat Hanh (2008) says, when we are fully present in an activity such as cleaning our teeth or washing-up, not only does it become quite nourishing but also it is a great vehicle for mindfulness practice. Of course, there are some things we have to do which we don't enjoy, but even then, bringing awareness to our judgements and the mental chatter (which compounds the dislike) can be adjusted to make it less depleting.

Lesson Plan: Session 5	
Session aim: To bring together the learning of the past 4 weeks by introducing the concept of loving kindness	
Objectives: 1. Students share with each other the activities that nourish them 2. Discuss the idea of loving kindness (to the self) 3. Students set intentions for how they will incorporate mindfulness practice into their everyday lives	
Activities:	**Time:**
1. Final meditation (loving kindness)	20 minutes
2. Enquiry	15 minutes
3. Feedback from noticing stress in the body	10 minutes
4. Feedback from Sounds and Thoughts Meditation	20 minutes
5. Feedback from nourishing and depleting activities	20 minutes
6. Preparing for difficult times	10 minutes
7. Loving kindness	10 minutes

Notes:

1. This week's meditation brings together all of the meditations that we have practised during the 5 week course and adds loving kindness.

2. Feedback from final meditation: how has your experience of mindful meditation changed over the 5 week course? If students set their intentions for this course at the beginning, you can remind them of these and ask them to reflect on what has changed.

3. The body in stress usually folds in on itself and tenses, the emotions go into a sense of fear or overwhelm, and the mind becomes very active. Your system is flooded with thoughts and connections. It is often at these times that we can begin to ruminate – thinking about the same thing over and over again.

4. Last week's meditation was sounds and thoughts, so ask students to recall the sounds which were present during their meditation and the thoughts they associate with those sounds. Explain how naming thoughts helps to disassociate from automatic reaction and allows time to make a wise choice.

5. Review all the things that nourish you; can you do more of them? Or, maybe notice what it is about the things that nourish you and see if they could bring this attitude to other activities.

6. In difficult times when you feel stressed, overwhelmed or panicked, try the breathing space and attach to it something which nourishes you as a reward. Or, if you are feeling down or procrastinating, follow the breathing space with a very small activity which gives you a sense of control. Remember when you are down or anxious, action always precedes motivation. If we wait for motivation it just might not come, so we must prompt it with a small action.

7. Explain that what we have been practising in these past weeks is loving kindness to the self, which, if continued can be extended to others and to the planet. End with a short breathing space and repeat of the loving kindness verse, 'May you be safe, May you be happy, May you be well, May you be free from suffering, May you come to love and accept all that you are, May you live with ease, May you know joy.'

Homework:

As this is the last week there is no formal homework, but it is useful to give students a set of questions to think about:

1. How will you continue your mindfulness practice?
2. What might get in the way of your mindfulness practice?
3. What nourishes you?
4. What one thing have you found most useful during this 5 week course?

Remember the important ingredients of mindfulness to help with study:

- If possible, at first signs of stress or anxiety, – *Pause.* Do the breathing space.
- Watch your posture and do a power pose (e.g. unclench fists, jaw, etc.).
- Watch for your thoughts: *Are you following thoughts which do not serve you?*
- Be kind to yourself. If you are telling yourself off with a harsh and unkind voice, if you are about to get to a very negative place – remember it won't help you, it can increase your anxiety, it won't make you take more responsibility.

- Bring a sense of kindness and compassion to yourself with the posture and breathing space for just five breaths. It will help you make a wiser decision about what to do next. It will help open the hippocampus for memory and help you to think using your prefrontal cortex for the higher more reasonable thoughts rather than the impulses or the total closing down of the amygdala.
- Remember the mouse in the maze. Choose to go down the reward rather than the avoidant pathway which closes your thinking capacity down but can send you on a roller coaster of ruminative 'what ifs' and take you right off track.
- Remember the brain needs to rest and switch off for a while to work at its best. The brain is not replenished by sleep like all the other organs, so you need to actively rest it for a few minutes every now and then, just by stopping your thoughts and breathing. *If you are too anxious to sleep, remember that practising mindfulness is very restorative for the brain and body.*

Resources

Healthy Minds Project: https://www.projecthealthyminds.com/
History's 30 most inspiring people on the autistic spectrum: https://www.appliedbehavioranalysisprograms.com/historys-30-most-inspiring-people-on-the-autism-spectrum/
Myers Briggs Type Indicator: https://www.myersbriggs.org/my-mbti-personality-type/mbti-basics/

References

Briggs Myers, I. and Myers, P. (2010) *Gifts Differing: Understanding Personality Type*, 2nd revised edition. Mountain View, CA: Davies-Black.

Goleman, D. and Davidson, R. (2017) *Altered Traits: Science Reveals How Meditation Changes Your Mind, Brain and Body*. New York: Avery Publishing.

Honey, P. and Mumford, A. (2012) *Learning Styles Questionnaire*. London: Pearson Education.

Oliver, T. (2020) *The Self Delusion: The Surprising Science of Our Connection to Each Other and the Natural World*. London: Weidenfeld & Nicolson.

Thich Nhat Hanh (2008) *The Miracle of Mindfulness: The Classic Guide to Mindfulness from the World's Most Revered Master*. London: Rider.

Conclusion

Student perspective 4

"I first came into contact with mindfulness during my placement year in 2017/18 at a course run for parents of patients. Having no real prior knowledge, I was not sure it was for me and bought into the common misconceptions of mindfulness that it is 'meditation and hippy dippy'. However, understanding the impact upon parents of patients and working with the mindfulness group changed my opinions.

I think I learnt that mindfulness is for everyone – whether they are informal or formal practices! In the beginning it may take time to develop the practice like anything else that is new, but with time it can be helpful. I have used practices to help me through my own mental health struggles as well as other forms of support. Being non-judgemental with yourself and having a different relationship with your emotions and reactions though mindfulness is such a help at times." (Natalie Potts, Psychology student)

As we come to the end of this book, we hope that we have managed to convey some of the essence of mindfulness to help you understand yourself, your motivations and your habits better. Mindfulness can liberate us and open our perceptions each day to the greater wonders of the world around us. Reading this book may have helped you to start to create new habits in your thinking and your life. We hope to have managed to whet your appetite in order to try to follow the teachings and practices of mindfulness. You may even have gained enough insight and practical skills to start to control your body and mind a little bit more when you need to. If you have been changed and intrigued by the process of mindfulness, you may even be on a journey to become one of the next generation of mindfulness teachers.

To summarise the aspects of mindfulness which can help students, we will look at how mindfulness links with the findings on how to live a good life. First, we will review how the practices fit in with ideas from philosophy, health and religion. We will address some of the causes of loneliness, depression and anxiety that are so prevalent in twenty-first century Western society. This chapter draws on information from such ancient philosophers as Aristotle and traditional religious teachings, as well as the latest scientific research on happiness by Caroline Ryff and Laurie Santos.

Aristotle claimed the goal of life is *eudaimonia* – a quality of *flourishing* by finding 'the right means' to a balanced place between risky impulsiveness and cowardice. The term flourishing is now closely associated with the modern understanding of 'wellbeing'. He said this could be achieved through self-monitoring, which is the ongoing practice of noting our thoughts and acts (Aristotle, cited by Goleman and Davidson, 2017). The Stoics went on to develop this by recognising that our *feelings* about life events, not the events themselves, determine our happiness. The Ancient Greeks taught the regular practice of exercises and self-discipline as the pathway to cultivating equanimity and the insight to distinguish between the things we can and cannot change. They believed this would help people develop traits in thoughts and actions of kindness, integrity, compassion, patience and humility to foster a sense of wellbeing and cultivate harmony. This way of thinking is mirrored in Eastern traditions such as Hinduism and Buddhism, which advocate cultivating practices that set us on the path to *self-actualisation*. In many ways, Buddhism is the philosophy to most influence mindfulness because it provides a comprehensive methodology about how to be more mindful and conscious in our lives.

A model of six criteria of wellbeing based on Aristotle's ancient teaching was created by Ryff in 1989. This is a summary of his model:

1 **Self-acceptance:** being positive about yourself; acknowledging both your good and bad qualities and adopting non-judgemental self-awareness.
2 **Personal growth:** sensing that you get better as you age and develop towards your full potential, which combines acceptance with growth.
3 **Autonomy:** developing independence in thought and deed, freedom from social pressure and being true to your own value systems (this is very important in more individualistic cultures).
4 **Mastery:** feeling competent to handle life's complexities, seizing opportunities and creating situations that satisfy your needs and values.
5 **Satisfying relationships:** establishing relationships and connections with others that provide warmth, empathy and trust with mutual give-and-take.
6 **Life purpose:** having goals and beliefs that give a sense of meaning and direction.

More recently, Laurie Santos (2021) designed a course at Yale after she became a Head of College. She witnessed the high levels of student distress, unhappiness and loneliness that are mirrored in much of the current research on students' wellbeing. Santos' experience is backed-up in a recent survey by the American College Health Association (2018). It reported that more than 40 per cent of US students were so depressed that they found it difficult to function, more than 60 per cent had experienced overwhelming anxiety, and more than 1 in 10 had seriously considered suicide in the previous year. The course, *The Science of Wellbeing,* was based on her experience of living amongst students on campus and witnessing first-hand the behaviour of high-attaining students outside of the classroom. It contained practical techniques and tips on how to address stress and live with a greater sense of wellbeing. The course proved extremely popular; just under 25 per cent of the entire student body at Yale signed up. A 6 week version of the course is available free online (see the list of resources below).

These are the key points of Santos' course:

1 **Stay present:** try not to wish your life away.
2 **Practise gratitude:** notice pleasant events rather than dwell on negative experiences.
3 **Stay connected to the body:** try to be as fit and healthy as you can be.
4 **Acknowledge and explore negative emotions:** rather than running away from them under the guise of negative defence mechanisms.

For students, the lessons here are clear. Try to connect with people on your programme of study. Join groups and societies offered by your Students' Union which will help you to meet like-minded people, or set up a society of your own that reflects your interests if one is not on offer. Volunteer your time on projects or events which you have an interest in. Try to notice pleasant events and try not to dwell on negative emotions. Take advantage of the sports facilities available at your campus, or at least build in daily walks on which you cultivate an awareness of nature and the built environment. Try to structure your days to establish a regular sleep pattern and eat at least one healthy meal a day. If there is a mindfulness society on your campus, join it. If there isn't, try to establish one and connect with the university counselling, mental health and wellbeing team.

We feel very privileged to work amongst a host of students and young people who want to make a difference. The students we meet at mindfulness groups want to work on themselves and to reflect on the social and ecological issues of our time. To summarise, in order to live a good life, we need to have:

1 A sense of meaning and purpose
2 A sense of belonging: connection to ourselves, each other and nature
3 A belief in our future
4 A means to choose to respond rather than react
5 A shared value system and as best we can live in accordance with that value system
6 A sense of autonomy to believe we can manage and regulate our thoughts, bodies and emotions
7 A compassion towards ourselves and others
8 A curiosity and interest in life as opposed to judgemental opinions
9 A means to evoke the relaxation response for difficult times through rituals such as meditation, prayer, movement, exercise, singing, etc
10 A means to cultivate acceptance, happiness and joy.

Through our experience of running mindfulness groups on campus and online, we have learned that students and young people have a sense of awe about the world. In the early days of the Mindfulness Society, we ran groups at lunchtime or in the early evening. The students sat or lay on mats and snuggled under blankets. As they crossed the threshold of the room, a quiet descended and the values

Figure 2: Diagram by Faith Turton

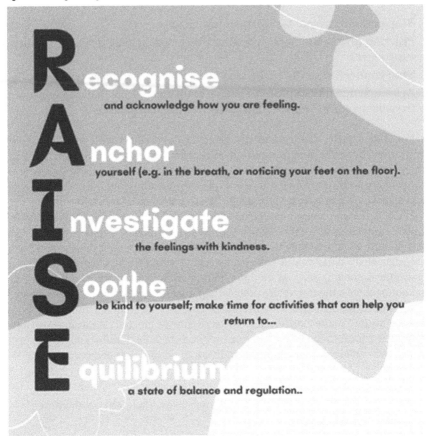

and qualities of mindfulness connected us. Sharing the values of curiosity, compassion, patience and being non-judgemental, we entered the sanctity of the meditation. Afterwards, in the honest sharing of our humanness, we heard stories of racing thoughts being still for a while, of restlessness transforming into feelings of peace, and of sadness giving way to moments of acceptance.

During 2020/21 we had to move online. Luckily, the sense of community and mindfulness has been sustained and extended; students who had not attended previously were able to join in from the comfort of their own room. Often, we start a session with a short introductory story and then invite members of the group to evoke a sense of self-compassion and acceptance by 'dropping into the now'. Through their shared mindfulness practice, students can bring patience and kindness and curiosity. Perhaps we should leave the last word to the students. They created the acronym RAISE. It is a reminder of how to come back to your centre when you are feeling out of balance.

We hope this book may help to spread the word about mindfulness to future generations of students.

"Given my conditioning and upbringing in a Western country, in which productivity and ambition are the name of the game, mindfulness seemed very foreign to me at first. However, through regular practice, I have come to understand, not only that, I am just as worthy as any other human being, but also that happiness is not conditional, and it is not to be chased. Instead, it is a gift available to us all when we let go of worries about how we think we are supposed to feel or where we are supposed to be in our lives.

As we pause and notice our breath with curiosity, we remove any filters of black or white to see ourselves through an attitude of acceptance. In this way, we allow the present moment to magically unfold before our eyes, unlocking precious opportunities for joy and simple clarity to be found in our hearts. In these moments of infinite spaciousness, we may find seeds of happiness placed in the centre of ourselves and we experience their wonderful growth as we make the conscious choice to nurture them each day. In this way, we witness the blooming of a lush garden of loving kindness to be joyfully shared with others. Hence, one of the most valuable lessons of mindfulness has been to become our own most loyal companion. This has led me to fully embrace all of life's experiences, whether pleasant or unpleasant, with unconditional loving resilience." (Asia Charles, Psychology student)

Resources

The Science of Well-being (online course) https://www.coursera.org/learn/the-science-of-well-being

References

American College Health Association (2018) Available at: https://www.acha.org/documents/ncha/NCHA-II_Fall_2018_Reference_Group_Executive_Summary.pdf

Goleman, D. and Davidson, R. (2017) *Altered Traits: Science Reveals How Meditation Changes Your Mind, Brain and Body*. New York: Avery Publishing.

Ryff, C. (1989) Happiness is everything, or is it? Explorations on the meaning of psychological well-being, *Journal of Personality and Social Psychology*, 57 (6): 1069–1081.

Santos, L. (2021) The Surprising Truth about Happiness. Feel Better: Live more [Podcast], *YouTube*, 27 January. Available at: https://www.youtube.com/watch?v=dthI6xZ_CrM

Index

Page numbers in italics are figures; with 't' are tables.